Math Bridge

6th grade

Written by:

Tracy Dankberg & James Michael Orr

Project Directors: Michele D. Van Leeuwen
Scott G. Van Leeuwen

Creative & Marketing Director: George Starks

Design & Technical Project Director: Dante J. Orazzi

TABLE OF CONTENTS

INTRODUCTION

The *Math Bridge* series is designed to help students improve their mathematical skills in all areas. This book has been developed to provide sixth grade students with skill-based exercises in the following areas: whole numbers; decimals; number theory; fractions; ratio and proportion; percent; geometry; measurement; integers; pre-algebra; probability and statistics. The purpose of this book, therefore, is to strengthen students' mathematical concepts, thus helping them to become better mathematicians and to improve achievement test scores.

Math Bridge includes many extras to help your students in their study of mathematics. For instance,

✔ An Incentive Contract begins the book to motivate students to complete their work.

✔ A diagnostic test has been included to help assess your students' mathematical knowledge.

✔ Exercises become progressively more difficult as students work through the book.

✔ Tips are included throughout the book as reminders to help students successfully complete their work.

✔ Thought-provoking questions (Think About It) are periodically placed throughout the book to emphasize critical thinking skills.

✔ Additional exercises are included to help students in practicing with estimation.

✔ The exercises prepare students for standardized achievement tests.

✔ Each section includes problem-solving exercises written with the purpose of reinforcing the skills taught in that section.

Mathematics is all around us and is an essential part of life. It is the authors' intention that through the completion of this book, students will come away with a stronger knowledge of mathematics to assist them both inside and outside of the classroom.

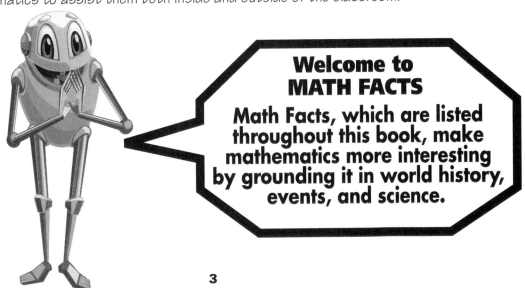

Welcome to MATH FACTS

Math Facts, which are listed throughout this book, make mathematics more interesting by grounding it in world history, events, and science.

Incentive Contract

In • cen'tive, *n*. **1.** Something that urges a person on. **2.** Enticing. **3.** Encouraging. **4.** That which excites to action or moves the mind.

LIST YOUR AGREED-UPON INCENTIVE FOR EACH SECTION BELOW

Place a ✔ after each activity upon completion

Students Signature _____

PG	Activity Title	✔
9	Place Value	
10	Writing Numbers in Standard Form	
11	Rounding Numbers	
12	Estimating	
13	Addition	
14	Subtraction	
15	Multiplication	
16	Division	
17	Order of Operations	
18	Problem Solving	

MY INCENTIVE IS ✖

19	Place Value	
20	Writing	
21	Rounding	
22	Comparing and Ordering	
23	Estimating	
24	Adding & Subtracting	
26	Problem Solving	
27	Estimating Products	
28	Multiplying by 10, 100, & 1000	
29	Multiplying	
30	More Multiplying	
31	Estimating Quotients	
32	Dividing by 10, 100, & 1000	
33	Dividing by Whole Numbers	
34	Dividing by Decimals	
35	Scientific Notation	
36	Problem Solving	

MY INCENTIVE IS ✖

37	Exponents	
38	Prime & Composite Numbers	
39	Prime Factorization	
40	Greatest Common Factor	
41	Least Common Multiple	
42	Problem Solving	

MY INCENTIVE IS ✖

43	Equivalent Fractions	
44	Reducing Fractions	
45	Comparing & Ordering	
46	Improper Fractions & Mixed Numbers	
47	Fractions as Decimals	
48	Adding and Subtracting	
51	Problem Solving	
52	Multiplying Fractions & Mixed Numbers	
53	Dividing Fractions & Mixed Numbers	
54	Problem Solving	

MY INCENTIVE IS ✖

Teacher or Parent Signature _____

55	Reading Charts & Tables	
56	Graphing Skills	
57	Predicting Outcomes	
58	Mean, Median & Mode	

MY INCENTIVE IS ✖

59	Understanding Percent	
60	Writing Decimals as Percents	
61	Writing Fractions as Percents	
62	Percents, Fractions & Decimals	
63	Percent of a Number	
64	Problem Solving	

MY INCENTIVE IS ✖

65	Classifying Angles	
66	Classifying Quadrilaterals	
67	Classifying Triangles	
68	Symmetry	
69	Congruent & Similar Figures	

MY INCENTIVE IS ✖

70	Customary System	
71	Computing Customary Units	
72	The Metric System	
73	Problem Solving	
74	Perimeter & Area of Quadrilaterals	
75	Perimeter & Area of Triangles	
76	Circumference & Area of Circles	

MY INCENTIVE IS ✖

77	Understanding Integers	
78	Comparing & Ordering	
79	Adding Integers	
80	Subtracting Integers	
81	Multiplying & Dividing	
82	Problem Solving	

MY INCENTIVE IS ✖

83	Evaluating Algebraic Equations	
84	Solving Equations with + & −	
85	Solving Equations with x & ÷	
86	Problem Solving	

MY INCENTIVE IS ✖

87	Chances & Probability	
88	Making Tree Diagrams	
89	Reading Graphs	
90	Mean, Median & Mode	
91	Problem Solving	

MY INCENTIVE IS ✖

DIAGNOSTIC TEST

Name_____ Score _____

Directions: Read the following problems. For each question, fill in the circle of the correct answer. If the correct answer is not given, fill in the answer space marked **N** (Not Given).

1. $449 + 478 =$ ○ A. 926   ○ B. 927   ○ C. 827   ○ D. 928

2. $594 - 198 =$ ○ A. 392   ○ B. 398   ○ C. 396   ○ D. N

3. $42 \times 22 =$ ○ A. 904   ○ B. 924   ○ C. 944   ○ D. N

4. $432 \div 18 =$ ○ A. 22.2   ○ B. 23   ○ C. 24.2   ○ D. 24

5. $8 + (3 \times 9) =$ ○ A. 34   ○ B. 35   ○ C. 99   ○ D. 216

6. $346 \times 4{,}000 =$ ○ A. 1,384   ○ B. 13,840   ○ C. 138,400   ○ D. N

7. $1.6 + .25 =$ ○ A. 4.1   ○ B. .41   ○ C. 1.85   ○ D. 18.5

8. $52.78 - 38.24 =$ ○ A. 14.44   ○ B. 14.54   ○ C. 14.64   ○ D. N

9. $3.417 \div 2.01 =$ ○ A. 1.7   ○ B. .17   ○ C. .017   ○ D. N

10. $4.5 \times .16 =$ ○ A. 7.2   ○ B. .72   ○ C. .072   ○ D. N

11. $.02 \div 4 =$ ○ A. .005   ○ B. .05   ○ C. .5   ○ D. 5

---

12. What is the closest estimate of $483 - 309$?
   ○ A. 100   ○ B. 150   ○ C. 200   ○ D. 250

13. The closest estimate of 41×30 is what?
   ○ A. 70   ○ B. 130   ○ C. 1,200   ○ D. 1,300

14. What is the closest estimate of $4{,}321 + 3{,}873$?
   ○ A. 5,000   ○ B. 6,000   ○ C. 7,000   ○ D. 8,000

15. The closest estimate of $\$48.25 \div 7$ is what?
   ○ A. $5.00   ○ B. $6.00   ○ C. $7.00   ○ D. N

16. What is the closest estimate of $\$681.51 - \$326.73$?
   ○ A. $300   ○ B. $400   ○ C. $500   ○ D. $600

DIAGNOSTIC TEST

Name _____

17. What is another way to write 42?

    ○ A. $(6 \times 6) + 6$ ○ B. $(8 \times 6) - 7$ ○ C. $(3 \times 9) \times 2$ ○ D. N

18. What are the factors of 18?

    ○ A. 2, 4, 6, 18   ○ B. 1, 2, 4, 6, 18   ○ C. 1, 2, 3, 6, 9, 18   ○ D. N

19. Which number has a **6** in the thousandths place?

    ○ A. 10.613   ○ B. 6000.36   ○ C. 10.316   ○ D. 10.163

20. Complete the following equation or inequality to make a true statement. $\frac{1}{2} + 4 \bigcirc \frac{3}{4} + 4$

    ○ A. <   ○ B. >   ○ C. =   ○ D. N

21. Which of the following numerals is the same as $\frac{6}{9}$?

    ○ A. $\frac{1}{2}$ ○ B. $\frac{3}{4}$ ○ C. $\frac{2}{3}$ ○ D. $\frac{5}{8}$

22. Looking at the word *football*, what fraction of the total number of letters is vowels?

    ○ A. $\frac{1}{2}$ ○ B. $\frac{1}{3}$ ○ C. $\frac{3}{8}$ ○ D. $\frac{5}{8}$

23. Which one of the following decimals is equal to $\frac{3}{4}$?

    ○ A. .25   ○ B. .34   ○ C. .50   ○ D. N

24. What would you replace the <u>x</u> with in the following equation? $\frac{2}{x} \times \frac{3}{3} = \frac{6}{15}$

    ○ A. 5   ○ B. 4   ○ C. 3   ○ D. 6

25. Look at the following fractions in the box. How many are greater than $\frac{1}{2}$?

$$\frac{5}{12}, \frac{7}{16}, \frac{2}{3}, \frac{6}{12}, \frac{3}{4}, \frac{3}{8}, \frac{5}{8}$$

    ○ A. 3   ○ B. 4   ○ C. 5   ○ D. 6

26. What is $3\frac{1}{4}$ written as an improper fraction?

    ○ A. $\frac{12}{4}$ ○ B. $\frac{12}{6}$ ○ C. $\frac{13}{6}$ ○ D. $\frac{13}{4}$

27. $\frac{1}{8} + \frac{4}{8} =$

    ○ A. $\frac{5}{8}$ ○ B. $\frac{3}{4}$ ○ C. $\frac{5}{16}$ ○ D. $\frac{3}{8}$

28. $\dfrac{1}{10} + \dfrac{3}{8} =$

     ○ A. $\dfrac{1}{2}$ ○ B. $\dfrac{4}{18}$ ○ C. $\dfrac{19}{40}$ ○ D. $\dfrac{21}{40}$

29. $\dfrac{3}{6} - \dfrac{1}{6} =$

     ○ A. $\dfrac{1}{6}$ ○ B. $\dfrac{1}{2}$ ○ C. $\dfrac{1}{3}$ ○ D. $\dfrac{2}{3}$

30. $\dfrac{2}{5} \times \dfrac{1}{3} =$

     ○ A. $\dfrac{1}{2}$ ○ B. $\dfrac{1}{15}$ ○ C. $\dfrac{1}{5}$ ○ D. $\dfrac{3}{4}$

31. $\dfrac{2}{4} \times \dfrac{2}{5} =$

     ○ A. $\dfrac{4}{15}$ ○ B. $\dfrac{4}{9}$ ○ C. $\dfrac{1}{5}$ ○ D. $\dfrac{1}{10}$

32. $1\dfrac{2}{3} \times 6\dfrac{1}{2} =$

     ○ A. $10\dfrac{5}{6}$ ○ B. $6\dfrac{1}{3}$ ○ C. $10\dfrac{1}{6}$ ○ D. N

33. Which of the following pairs of fractions forms a proportion?

     ○ A. $\dfrac{6}{16}, \dfrac{3}{8}$ ○ B. $\dfrac{5}{8}, \dfrac{4}{6}$ ○ C. $\dfrac{6}{9}, \dfrac{8}{11}$ ○ D. $\dfrac{5}{7}, \dfrac{18}{27}$

34. In Shante's neighborhood, the ratio of cats to dogs is 1 to 2. If there are 14 dogs, how many cats are there?

     ○ A. 14   ○ B. 21   ○ C. 7   ○ D. 18

35. Which of the following percents is equal to $\dfrac{8}{100}$?

     ○ A. .8%   ○ B. 8%   ○ C. 80%   ○ D. 800%

36. Which of the following decimals is equal to 42%?

     ○ A. .042   ○ B. .42   ○ C. 4.2   ○ D. 42

37. What is 25% of 24?

     ○ A. 4   ○ B. 5   ○ C. 6   ○ D. 7

38. Sarah left her house at 7:15 a.m. for school. If she returned from school at 4:45 p.m., how long was she away from home?

    ○ A. $8\frac{1}{2}$ hours   ○ B. $9\frac{1}{2}$ hours   ○ C. $10\frac{1}{2}$ hours   ○ D. $11\frac{1}{2}$ hours

39. At the spring book sale, Cynthia ordered a three-volume set of books for $31.25, instead of paying $12.95 for each of the three books. By buying the set, how much money did she save?

    ○ A. $6.60   ○ B. $7.60   ○ C. $7.50   ○ D. $8.50

40. What is the perimeter of the rectangle? 4 in

    10 in

    ○ A. 14 in   ○ B. 30 in   ○ C. 28 in   ○ D. 24 in

41. Name the figure at the right. ←———→

    ○ A. point   ○ B. segment   ○ C. ray   ○ D. line

42. Classify the angle at the right.

    ○ A. acute   ○ B. right   ○ C. obtuse   ○ D. straight

43. If there are 12 eggs in 1 dozen, how many eggs are there in 7 dozen?

    ○ A. 72   ○ B. 84   ○ C. 96   ○ D. 108

44. Mrs. Moody collected $5.75 from each one of her students for the field trip. If she has 26 students in her class, approximately how much did she collect?

    ○ A. $180   ○ B. $130   ○ C. $260   ○ D. N

45. The width of a football field would most likely be measured in which units?

    ○ A. liters   ○ B. millimeters   ○ C. kilometers   ○ D. meters

46. Tom has 12 black chips and 14 red chips in a bucket. If he chooses one chip from the bucket, what are the chances of choosing a red one?

    ○ A. 7/13   ○ B. 6/13   ○ C. 8/13   ○ D. 9/13

47. What is the average of the following numbers?   12, 4, 6, 2

    ○ A. 11   ○ B. 6   ○ C. 7   ○ D. 8

48. Which numeral below makes the number sentence *true*? $x < .8$

    ○ A. 7   ○ B. 7.7   ○ C. .7   ○ D. N

49. If $x + 15 = 27$, then x is what?

    ○ A. 7   ○ B. 10   ○ C. 12   ○ D. 13

50. If $y - 8 = 21$, then y is what?

    ○ A. 29   ○ B. 13   ○ C. 31   ○ D. 19

Whole Numbers: Place Value

Name _____

Write the value of each underlined digit. Study the chart below.

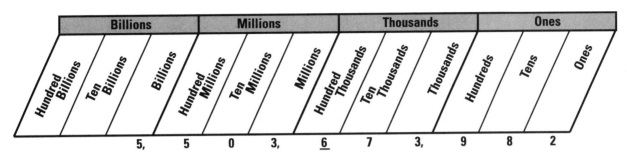

Billions			Millions			Thousands			Ones		
Hundred Billions	Ten Billions	Billions	Hundred Millions	Ten Millions	Millions	Hundred Thousands	Ten Thousands	Thousands	Hundreds	Tens	Ones
		5,	5	0	3,	<u>6</u>	7	3,	9	8	2

The underlined digit 6 is in the hundred thousands place. So it has a place value of <u>600 thousand</u>.

---

1. 1,3<u>8</u>5

    _____

2. 62,<u>9</u>99

    _____

3. 59,67<u>8</u>

    _____

4. 4<u>3</u>0,581

    _____

5. 755,<u>4</u>83

    _____

6. <u>6</u>73,902

    _____

7. 64,<u>0</u>02,941

    _____

8. <u>1</u>4,578,104

    _____

9. <u>1</u>56,747,251

    _____

10. <u>4</u>06,383,765

    _____

11. 3<u>2</u>2,281,324

    _____

12. 24<u>1</u>,587,860

    _____

13. 8<u>7</u>,563,930,501

    _____

14. 3<u>1</u>2,654,201,150

    _____

15. <u>8</u>4,698,502,180

    _____

 THINK ABOUT IT!

16. Write two 9-digit numbers so that one is exactly one million more than the other.

9

Whole Numbers: Writing Numbers in Standard Form

Write each number in standard form.

three thousand, eight hundred forty-one.   <u>3,841</u>

TIP: *Don't forget to use a comma to separate each group of three digits.*

1. seven thousand, two hundred sixty _____

2. sixty-three thousand, four hundred thirty-seven _____

3. thirty-three thousand, three hundred three _____

4. forty-nine thousand, four hundred forty-nine _____

5. seventy-one thousand, ninety-seven _____

6. eighty-thousand, fourteen _____

7. fifty-two thousand, six _____

8. forty-five thousand, forty-five _____

9. three hundred seventy-five thousand, one hundred seventy-five _____

10. one hundred twenty-three thousand, eight hundred eighty-one _____

11. five hundred fifty-four thousand, six hundred one _____

12. two hundred two thousand, one hundred fifty-four _____

13. six million, six hundred thousand, three hundred twenty-one _____

14. eighty million, two hundred fifty thousand, three hundred two _____

15. two hundred thirty million, five hundred nine thousand, three _____

Whole Numbers: Rounding Numbers   Name _____

Round each number to the underlined place value position.

1<u>3</u>7

↓

140

Look to the right of 3. If that number is 5 or greater, round up. If not, keep the number the same, and change all numbers to the right to zeros.

---

1.   <u>9</u>3
_____

2.   <u>5</u>18
_____

3.   <u>6</u>83
_____

4.   2<u>9</u>4
_____

5.   3,<u>6</u>42
_____

6.   <u>4</u>,560
_____

7.   5,<u>9</u>70
_____

8.   36,<u>7</u>51
_____

9.   <u>7</u>4,659
_____

10. 62,<u>2</u>41
_____

11. <u>5</u>5,210
_____

12. 24,<u>9</u>40
_____

13. <u>6</u>7,005
_____

14. 5<u>1</u>,998
_____

15. <u>5</u>9,2034
_____

16. <u>3</u>01,650
_____

17. 682,<u>5</u>04
_____

18. <u>2</u>9,549
_____

19. 189,<u>0</u>55
_____

20. <u>7</u>03,295
_____

 THINK ABOUT IT!

21. Would it make sense to round a friend's phone number? The age of an ancient piece of pottery? Explain.

Whole Numbers: Estimating

Name _____

Estimate each sum or difference. **Watch the sign!**

Nearest Ten	*Nearest Hundred*	*Nearest Thousand*
68 ↑ 70	319 ↑ 300	8,765 ↑ 9,000
+41 ↑ 40	+687 ↑ 700	−2,103 ↑ 2,000
Estimate 110	Estimate 1,000	Estimate 7,000

---

1. 82
    −27

2. 68
    −12

3. 39
    +13

4. 51
    +19

5. 73
    −22

6. 25
    +37

7. 689
    −312

8. 430
    +297

9. 689
    +103

10. 477
     −392

11. 521
     − 98

12. 743
     +681

13. 9,873
     −3,210

14. 2,361
     +2,893

15. 4,936
     −3,130

16. 8,387
     −1,238

17. 3,985
     −2,116

18. 6,580
     +2,930

19. 2,150
     +3,895

20. 1,750
     −1,135

 THINK ABOUT IT!

21. A local charity has a goal of raising $10,000 during its fundraising drive. So far, the charity has collected $6,893. <u>About</u> how much more money is needed to reach the goal?

Whole Numbers: Addition

Name _____

Add: 6,591 + 5,263

1. Line up the numbers.
2. Start with the ones place.
3. Carry (trade) if necessary.

```
  6,591
 +5,263
 11,854
```

$\left\langle$ 15 tens = 1 hundred plus 5 tens $\right\rangle$

	A	B	C	D	E
1.	33 + 4	22 + 6	58 + 5	36 + 8	68 + 4
2.	34 +25	46 +23	273 +14	328 +52	643 +59
3.	532 +321	618 +201	754 +366	1,054 +971	3,259 +681
4.	4,322 +3,615	5,371 +2,425	43,650 +7,189	45,962 +6,184	65,395 +76,550

5. 65 + 8 =   72 + 65 =   325 + 67 =   658 + 283 =

6. 753 + 8 =   2,093 + 45 =   78 + 9,813 =   230 + 8 =

Whole Numbers: Subtraction

Name _____

Subtract.

Subtract 248 from 300.

1. Line up the numbers.
2. Start with the ones place.
3. Borrow if necessary.

$$\begin{array}{r} {}^{2\,9}\!\!\not{3}\!\not{0}\!\not{0}^{10} \\ -248 \\ \hline 52 \end{array}$$

---

1. $\begin{array}{r} 45 \\ -\ 3 \\ \hline \end{array}$
2. $\begin{array}{r} 37 \\ -\ 6 \\ \hline \end{array}$
3. $\begin{array}{r} 54 \\ -\ 4 \\ \hline \end{array}$
4. $\begin{array}{r} 84 \\ -\ 5 \\ \hline \end{array}$
5. $\begin{array}{r} 76 \\ -\ 8 \\ \hline \end{array}$

6. $\begin{array}{r} 34 \\ -21 \\ \hline \end{array}$
7. $\begin{array}{r} 65 \\ -30 \\ \hline \end{array}$
8. $\begin{array}{r} 87 \\ -33 \\ \hline \end{array}$
9. $\begin{array}{r} 56 \\ -46 \\ \hline \end{array}$
10. $\begin{array}{r} 47 \\ -28 \\ \hline \end{array}$

11. $\begin{array}{r} 253 \\ -42 \\ \hline \end{array}$
12. $\begin{array}{r} 685 \\ -39 \\ \hline \end{array}$
13. $\begin{array}{r} 400 \\ -87 \\ \hline \end{array}$
14. $\begin{array}{r} 595 \\ -497 \\ \hline \end{array}$
15. $\begin{array}{r} 783 \\ -598 \\ \hline \end{array}$

16. $\begin{array}{r} 5,316 \\ -215 \\ \hline \end{array}$
17. $\begin{array}{r} 4,920 \\ -875 \\ \hline \end{array}$
18. $\begin{array}{r} 7,601 \\ -3,945 \\ \hline \end{array}$
19. $\begin{array}{r} 8,200 \\ -6,590 \\ \hline \end{array}$
20. $\begin{array}{r} 2,756 \\ -1,766 \\ \hline \end{array}$

21. $\begin{array}{r} 56,214 \\ -5,294 \\ \hline \end{array}$
22. $\begin{array}{r} 70,954 \\ -4,961 \\ \hline \end{array}$
23. $\begin{array}{r} 20,806 \\ -17,607 \\ \hline \end{array}$
24. $\begin{array}{r} 57,230 \\ -31,175 \\ \hline \end{array}$
25. $\begin{array}{r} 61,548 \\ -10,753 \\ \hline \end{array}$

26. $62 - 9 =$
27. $73 - 15 =$
28. $591 - 28 =$
29. $653 - 545 =$

 THINK ABOUT IT!

30. Fill in the blanks:

$$\begin{array}{r} 7\ 8\ 1\ 3 \\ -\ \boxed{}\ \boxed{}\ \boxed{}\ \boxed{} \\ \hline 2\ 9\ 0\ 5 \end{array}$$

MATH FACTS
You probably know that construction and engineering use math to create our society, but did you know that artists and scientists also use math to learn and discover new things!

Whole Numbers: Multiplication

Name _____

Find the products. Study the examples below.

$$\begin{array}{r} 3 \\ 6,99\mathbf{6} \\ \times\ \ \ 6 \\ \hline 41,9\mathbf{76} \end{array}$$

6 × 6 = 3 tens and 6 ones

$$\begin{array}{r} 2 \\ 8,276 \\ \times\ \ \ 43 \\ \hline 24,828 \\ 331,040 \\ \hline 355,868 \end{array}$$

4 × 6 = 2 tens and 4 ones. Then write 4. Remember the 2.

1. $\begin{array}{r} 86 \\ \times\ 4 \\ \hline \end{array}$

2. $\begin{array}{r} 75 \\ \times\ 6 \\ \hline \end{array}$

3. $\begin{array}{r} 58 \\ \times\ 3 \\ \hline \end{array}$

4. $\begin{array}{r} 679 \\ \times\ 2 \\ \hline \end{array}$

5. $\begin{array}{r} 394 \\ \times\ 5 \\ \hline \end{array}$

6. $\begin{array}{r} 3,196 \\ \times\ 3 \\ \hline \end{array}$

7. $\begin{array}{r} 5,004 \\ \times\ 7 \\ \hline \end{array}$

8. $\begin{array}{r} 27,304 \\ \times\ 8 \\ \hline \end{array}$

9. $\begin{array}{r} 94 \\ \times\ 30 \\ \hline \end{array}$

10. $\begin{array}{r} 628 \\ \times\ 40 \\ \hline \end{array}$

11. $\begin{array}{r} 4,387 \\ \times\ 20 \\ \hline \end{array}$

12. $\begin{array}{r} 392 \\ \times\ 400 \\ \hline \end{array}$

13. $\begin{array}{r} 23 \\ \times\ 52 \\ \hline \end{array}$

14. $\begin{array}{r} 95 \\ \times\ 74 \\ \hline \end{array}$

15. $\begin{array}{r} 376 \\ \times\ 455 \\ \hline \end{array}$

16. $\begin{array}{r} 1,527 \\ \times\ 238 \\ \hline \end{array}$

17. $17 \times 24 =$

18. $27 \times 205 =$

19. $580 \times 62 =$

20. $2,431 \times 73 =$

 THINK ABOUT IT!

21. If you know that $40 \times 287 = 11,480$, how can you find 39×287 without multiplying?

15

Whole Numbers: Division

Name _____

Divide. Study the examples below before you begin the exercise.

$$140 \text{ R } 2$$
$$3 \overline{)422}$$
$$\underline{-3}$$
$$12$$
$$\underline{-12}$$
$$02$$
$$\underline{-0}$$
$$2$$

$$12 \div 3 = 4 \text{ R } 0$$

$$6 \text{ R } 17$$
$$72 \overline{)439}$$
$$\underline{-422}$$
$$17$$

$$439 \div 72$$

Think: $43 \div 7$ is close to 6

---

1. $3 \overline{)86}$

2. $6 \overline{)84}$

3. $7 \overline{)99}$

4. $4 \overline{)95}$

5. $9 \overline{)298}$

6. $4 \overline{)331}$

7. $6 \overline{)580}$

8. $2 \overline{)792}$

9. $60 \overline{)252}$

10. $20 \overline{)1,416}$

11. $67 \overline{)227}$

12. $76 \overline{)460}$

13. $85 \overline{)88,740}$

14. $62 \overline{)58,967}$

15. $25 \overline{)34,951}$

16. $92 \overline{)37,998}$

Whole Numbers: Order of Operations

Name _____

Solve the following problems. Remember to use the correct order of operations.

Order of operations:
1. Work inside the parentheses first.
2. Next, multiply and divide, *from left to right.*
3. Last, add and subtract, *from left to right.*

$$(13 - 3) \times 4 \qquad\qquad 13 - 3 \times 4$$
$$\underline{10 \times 4} \qquad\qquad\quad \underline{13 - 12}$$
$$40 \qquad\qquad\qquad\quad 1$$

1. $5 + 4 \times 2$

2. $(5 + 4) \times 2$

3. $(8 - 2) \times 3$

4. $8 - 2 \times 3$

5. $5 + 8 \div 2$

6. $6 \times (4 - 3)$

7. $6 \times 4 - 3$

8. $12 \div (3 + 1)$

9. $12 \div 3 + 1$

10. $6 + 10 \div 2$

11. $(6 + 10) \div 2$

12. $5 \times 3 + 4$

13. $5 \times (3 + 4)$

14. $4 + 5 \times 2$

15. $(4 + 5) \times 2$

16. $15 \div 3 + 2$

17. $15 \div (3 + 2)$

18. $18 - 8 \times 2$

19. $(18 - 8) \times 2$

20. $3 + 6 \times 4$

21. $(3 + 6) \times 4$

Problem Solving

Name _____

Solve each problem.

1. Karen watched 4 comedy shows, 3 drama shows, 2 movies, and 5 cartoons on TV one week. How many TV programs did Karen watch that week?

2. A 60-minute TV show had 48 minutes of show time and 12 minutes of scheduled commercials. How much longer was the show time than the commercials?

3. Grayson watched TV for 5 nights in one week. Each night he watched TV for 2 hours. How many hours did Grayson watch TV that week?

4. Tom spent $12 to rent 4 videotapes. How much did each rental cost?

5. At Chris' school, there were 38 students in the orchestra, 27 students in the band, and 42 students in the chorus. How many students were in the three groups?

6. Susie's class earned $360 for charity. The class decided to give the same amount each to four charities. How much will each charity receive?

7. In a basketball game, Michael made 13 two-point baskets and 4 three-point baskets. How many points did he score altogether?

8. There are 1,248 students enrolled at Henderson Middle School. Of these, 587 are boys. How many girls are enrolled at Henderson?

1.

2.

3.

4.

5.

6.

7.

8.

Decimals: Place Value

Name _____

Write the value of the underlined digit.

tens	ones	.	tenths	hundredths	thousandths	ten-thousandths	
	3	.	<u>5</u>	6			**5 tenths**
2	2	.	6	5	5	<u>4</u>	**4 ten-thousandths**

1. 63.21<u>8</u>

   _____

2. 8.4<u>2</u>17

   _____

3. 16.<u>8</u>96

   _____

4. 68.361<u>2</u>

   _____

5. 15.56<u>7</u>3

   _____

6. 5.8<u>7</u>3

   _____

7. 25.<u>9</u>826

   _____

8. 17.09<u>8</u>7

   _____

9. 6.165<u>9</u>

   _____

10. 13.4<u>3</u>2

   _____

11. 29.95<u>3</u>4

   _____

12. 7.<u>3</u>683

   _____

13. 537.4<u>68</u>

   _____

14. 5.351<u>6</u>

   _____

15. 83.246<u>7</u>

   _____

16. 99.6<u>7</u>34

   _____

17. 17.94<u>5</u>

   _____

18. 26.69<u>2</u>

   _____

19. 17.<u>8</u>081

   _____

20. 28.899<u>2</u>

   _____

21. 51.5<u>2</u>68

   _____

 THINK ABOUT IT!

22. Place a decimal point in the middle number so that all three numbers are in order, smallest to the largest.

   0.01, 0 0 3 8 4, .1   10, 4 7 6 5, 100

19

Decimals: Writing

Name _____

Write each number in standard form.

      one and forty-five hundredths <u>1.45</u>

1 Whole   45 out of 100

1. six and five tenths   _____

2. eleven and four tenths   _____

3. seven and two tenths   _____

4. fourteen and one tenth   _____

5. thirty-one and nine tenths   _____

6. nine and eighteen hundredths   _____

7. sixteen and thirty-seven hundredths   _____

8. forty-three and eight hundredths   _____

9. eighty-one and twenty-two hundredths   _____

10. two hundred and thirty-one hundredths   _____

11. forty-nine and forty-nine hundredths   _____

12. ten and twenty-seven hundredths   _____

13. three hundred five and one tenth   _____

14. twenty-eight and two hundred twelve thousandths   _____

15. eighteen and nine hundred sixty-one thousandths   _____

16. five hundred and two thousandths   _____

Decimals: Rounding

Name _____

Round each decimal to the underlined place-value position. Study the examples.

13.6<u>5</u>3 ⟶ **13.65**
(Drop the 3.)

<u>6</u>.79 ⟶ 7
(Drop the .79.)

Look to the right of the **5**. If that number is 5 or greater, *round up*. If not, keep the number the same. *Remember to drop all numbers past the rounded one.*

---

1. 141.3<u>6</u>7

   _____

2. 3<u>9</u>.987

   _____

3. 15.<u>3</u>15

   _____

4. 4.29<u>7</u>4

   _____

5. 0.<u>0</u>85

   _____

6. 27.7<u>9</u>1

   _____

7. 546.0<u>8</u>1

   _____

8. 3.<u>2</u>06

   _____

9. 13.0<u>7</u>6

   _____

10. 44<u>3</u>.788

    _____

11. 4.0<u>9</u>8

    _____

12. 607.<u>8</u>3

    _____

13. 16.65<u>3</u>8

    _____

14. 67.<u>2</u>6

    _____

15. <u>5</u>.568

    _____

16. 2.7<u>6</u>1

    _____

17. 5.<u>5</u>09

    _____

18. 6.2<u>9</u>45

    _____

19. 2<u>1</u>.04

    _____

20. 99.<u>3</u>8

    _____

21. 635.68<u>1</u>5

    _____

22. 59.<u>5</u>9

    _____

23. 1<u>7</u>.891

    _____

24. 53.<u>5</u>7

    _____

 THINK ABOUT IT!

25. It takes the moon an average of 27.32167 days to revolve around the Earth. Is the length of time closer to 27 or 28 days?

Decimals: Comparing and Ordering   **Name** _____

Write >, <, or = for each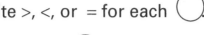

$$0.456 \bigcirc 0.462$$

0.456
0.462

5 < 6   so   0.456 < 0.462

To compare 2 or more decimals
1. Line up the decimal.
2. Compare digits from *left to right* in their corresponding place value.

---

1. 8.05 $\bigcirc$ 8.01

2. 0.390 $\bigcirc$ 0.039

3. 0.80 $\bigcirc$ 0.79

4. 0.032 $\bigcirc$ 0.0320

5. 0.007 $\bigcirc$ 0.01

6. 3.96 $\bigcirc$ 4.02

7. 2.5840 $\bigcirc$ 2.585

8. 11.226 $\bigcirc$ 11.326

9. 8.419 $\bigcirc$ 7.42

10. 6.019 $\bigcirc$ 6.019

11. 2.531 $\bigcirc$ 25.31

12. 62.9 $\bigcirc$ 63

Order from *least to greatest.*

13. 6.457, 6.45, 6.461, 6.46

14. 0.6, 0.06, 6.6, 0.606

15. 14.210, 14.201, 14.012, 14.120

16. 19.2, 1.92, 9.12, .912

17. 0.35, .035, 3.50, 3.05

18. 0.458, 0.4508, 0.4058, .0458

22

Decimals: Estimating

Name _____

Estimate each sum or difference. Use an appropriate strategy.

Estimate by rounding.

$$9.98 \longrightarrow 10$$
$$\underline{-4.13} \qquad \underline{-4}$$
$$\text{Estimate} \quad 6$$

Estimate by clustering.

$$61.1 + 59.8 + 60.9 =$$
$$60 \ + 60 \ + 60 \ = 60 \times 3 = 180$$
(The numbers all cluster around 60.)

---

1. $\begin{array}{r} 6.8 \\ 7.3 \\ +7.1 \\ \hline \end{array}$

2. $\begin{array}{r} 16.19 \\ -2.18 \\ \hline \end{array}$

3. $\begin{array}{r} 9.71 \\ +5.98 \\ \hline \end{array}$

4. $\begin{array}{r} 10.98 \\ -9.82 \\ \hline \end{array}$

5. $\begin{array}{r} 45.23 \\ +60.03 \\ \hline \end{array}$

6. $\begin{array}{r} 29.82 \\ 31.01 \\ +28.87 \\ \hline \end{array}$

7. $\begin{array}{r} 26.39 \\ -9.95 \\ \hline \end{array}$

8. $\begin{array}{r} 2.105 \\ +3.987 \\ \hline \end{array}$

9. $\begin{array}{r} 0.71 \\ -0.67 \\ \hline \end{array}$

10. $\begin{array}{r} 8.30 \\ +0.89 \\ \hline \end{array}$

11. $\begin{array}{r} 94.57 \\ -4.90 \\ \hline \end{array}$

12. $\begin{array}{r} 1.503 \\ +6.889 \\ \hline \end{array}$

13. $\begin{array}{r} 10.76 \\ 10.92 \\ 9.33 \\ +8.99 \\ \hline \end{array}$

14. $\begin{array}{r} 15.2 \\ 14.8 \\ +15.3 \\ \hline \end{array}$

15. $\begin{array}{r} 41.8 \\ 39.2 \\ 40.3 \\ +38.7 \\ \hline \end{array}$

16. $\begin{array}{r} 7.4 \\ 6.7 \\ 7.2 \\ +6.8 \\ \hline \end{array}$

17. $\begin{array}{r} 88.471 \\ -8.395 \\ \hline \end{array}$

18. $\begin{array}{r} 90.42 \\ +29.78 \\ \hline \end{array}$

19. $\begin{array}{r} 5.038 \\ -4.310 \\ \hline \end{array}$

20. $\begin{array}{r} 16.48 \\ +10.37 \\ \hline \end{array}$

21. $\begin{array}{r} 68.05 \\ -19.55 \\ \hline \end{array}$

22. $\begin{array}{r} 75.52 \\ +22.14 \\ \hline \end{array}$

23. $\begin{array}{r} 80.03 \\ -39.96 \\ \hline \end{array}$

24. $\begin{array}{r} 250.11 \\ +29.93 \\ \hline \end{array}$

25. $\begin{array}{r} 32.004 \\ +34.897 \\ \hline \end{array}$

26. $\begin{array}{r} 16.96 \\ -4.70 \\ \hline \end{array}$

27. $\begin{array}{r} 8.25 \\ -4.90 \\ \hline \end{array}$

28. $\begin{array}{r} 97.76 \\ -18.28 \\ \hline \end{array}$

Decimals: Adding & Subtracting

Name _____

Add or subtract. ***Watch the sign!***

17.6 + 37.83

$$\begin{array}{r} 17.60 \\ + \ 37.83 \\ \hline 55.43 \end{array}$$

1. Line up the decimal points
2. Add zeros if necessary.
3. Start from the ones place.
4. Carry (trade) if necessary.

TIP: *Remember to bring your decimal point down into your answer.*

---

1. $\begin{array}{r} 0.58 \\ + \ 0.4 \\ \hline \end{array}$

2. $\begin{array}{r} 13.75 \\ + \ 62.88 \\ \hline \end{array}$

3. $\begin{array}{r} 364.3 \\ - \ 121.44 \\ \hline \end{array}$

4. $\begin{array}{r} 803.01 \\ - \ 88.76 \\ \hline \end{array}$

5. $\begin{array}{r} 13.4267 \\ + \ 24.79 \\ \hline \end{array}$

6. $\begin{array}{r} 61.3 \\ - \ 17.85 \\ \hline \end{array}$

7. $\begin{array}{r} 6.004 \\ - \ 2.572 \\ \hline \end{array}$

8. $\begin{array}{r} 43.89 \\ + \ 9.49 \\ \hline \end{array}$

9. $\begin{array}{r} 0.54 \\ + \ 0.38 \\ \hline \end{array}$

10. $\begin{array}{r} 63.74 \\ - \ 17.26 \\ \hline \end{array}$

11. $\begin{array}{r} 0.362 \\ - \ 0.19 \\ \hline \end{array}$

12. $\begin{array}{r} 4.825 \\ + \ 3.769 \\ \hline \end{array}$

13. $\begin{array}{r} 475.3 \\ - \ 183.8 \\ \hline \end{array}$

14. $\begin{array}{r} 73.45 \\ + \ 16.49 \\ \hline \end{array}$

15. $\begin{array}{r} 32.7 \\ + \ 68.9 \\ \hline \end{array}$

16. $\begin{array}{r} 47.85 \\ + \ 34.6 \\ \hline \end{array}$

17. $\begin{array}{r} 0.763 \\ - \ 0.187 \\ \hline \end{array}$

18. $\begin{array}{r} 2.836 \\ + \ 1.39 \\ \hline \end{array}$

19. $\begin{array}{r} 703.7 \\ - \ 136.8 \\ \hline \end{array}$

20. $\begin{array}{r} 19.95 \\ - \ 7.79 \\ \hline \end{array}$

21. $\begin{array}{r} 100.00 \\ - \ 52.95 \\ \hline \end{array}$

22. $\begin{array}{r} 0.368 \\ + \ .875 \\ \hline \end{array}$

23. $\begin{array}{r} 4.68 \\ + \ 6.75 \\ \hline \end{array}$

24. $\begin{array}{r} 1.242 \\ - \ 0.368 \\ \hline \end{array}$

 THINK ABOUT IT!

25. Rachel has $50 to spend on a new outfit. She has found a blouse for $24.99 and a pair of shorts for $25.99. Does she have enough money to buy the blouse and shorts?

Decimals: Adding & Subtracting

Name _____

Add or subtract.

TIP: *Remember to line up the decimal points and add zeros if necessary.*

---

1. $4.7 + 8.8 =$

2. $0.472 - 0.0892 =$

3. $0.67 - 0.17 =$

4. $5.9 + 6.052 =$

5. $213.060 - 4.8 =$

6. $1.04 - 0.888 =$

7. $449.6 + 7.059 =$

8. $3.88 + .6 =$

9. $9.873 - 0.63 =$

10. $7.341 - 2.617 =$

11. $36.2 + 27.75 =$

12. $0.381 - .2 =$

13. $92.05 + 29.28 =$

14. $27.24 - 0.57 =$

15. $12.8 + 5.5 =$

16. $4.79 + 59.038 =$

17. $42 - 26.07 =$

18. $151.032 + 0.68 =$

THINK ABOUT IT!

19. Read the following statement. Tell whether it is **true** or **false**. Give examples to support your answer.

The sum of two decimals less than 1 is always less than 1.

Decimals: Problem Solving

Name _____

Solve each problem.

1. A pipe is 2.7518 cm in diameter. It needs to pass through a hole that is 2.7524 cm. Will it fit? By how much?

2. The tax on a soccer ball is $1.32. If the soccer ball cost $22.95, how much money will you need to buy the soccer ball?

3. The regular price of a pair of running shoes is $57.45. The shoes are on sale for $43.95. How much will you save by buying the shoes on sale?

4. Stacy bought a poster for $3.95 and a CD for $11.95. How much did she spend altogether before tax?

1.
2.
3.
4.

5. The squares below are called magic squares because each column, row, and diagonal adds to the same magic sum. Complete each magic square below.

	a.	
1.05		2.73
b.	c.	d.
	e.	
1.47		3.15

Magic Sum = 6.3

	f.	g.
0.65		
	h.	i.
1.35		
0.37	j.	0.93

Magic Sum = k._____

Decimals: Estimating Products

Name _____

Estimate each product. Use one of the two strategies designated below.

Estimate by rounding.	Estimate using compatible numbers.
32.96×3.83	26.52×4.13
$\downarrow \qquad \downarrow$	$\downarrow \qquad \downarrow$
$30 \quad \times \quad 4 = 120$	$25 \quad \times \quad 4 = 100$

Estimate by rounding.

1. $4.92 \times 8.29 =$

2. $3.826 \times 7.4 =$

3. $9.234 \times 6.7 =$

4. $26.3 \times 9.87 =$

5. $67.8 \times 9.65 =$

6. $2.8 \times 4.4 =$

7. $15.18 \times 2.31 =$

8. $3.6 \times 8.4 =$

9. $6.37 \times 7.29 =$

10. $9.35 \times 4.1 =$

11. $49.38 \times 6.1 =$

12. $70.27 \times 2.23 =$

Use compatible numbers.

13. $67.26 \times 38.95 =$

14. $312.3 \times 97.84 =$

15. $96.8 \times 5.7 =$

16. $18.97 \times 4.95 =$

17. $58.3 \times 1.9 =$

18. $24.67 \times 5.86 =$

19. $42.9 \times 9.8 =$

20. $17.9 \times 23.2 =$

21. $4.5 \times 26.53 =$

 THINK ABOUT IT!

22. Look at this product: $5{,}726 \times 684 = 3{,}916{,}584$.

Use estimation to choose A, B, or C as the correct answer to the problem below.

$$57.26 \times 6.84$$

○ A. 391.6548   ○ B. 3916.548   ○ C. 39.16548

Decimals: Multiplying by 10, 100, 1,000 Name _____

Study the example below. Then, complete the chart.

157.64 *Move decimal point*	**× 10** **1,576.4** *once* to the right.	**× 100** **15,764** *twice* to the right.	**× 1,000** **157,640** *3 times to the right*

TIP: *Add zeros to the end if necessary and do not write the decimal point if there are no numbers to the right. (See × 100 and × 1,000 above.)*

		× 10	× 100	× 1,000
1.	16.8792	_____	_____	_____
2.	8.9034	_____	_____	_____
3.	22.00154	_____	_____	_____
4.	36.835	_____	_____	_____
5.	58.678	_____	_____	_____
6.	71.0803	_____	_____	_____
7.	280.451	_____	_____	_____
8.	376.89	_____	_____	_____
9.	101.012	_____	_____	_____
10.	35.05	_____	_____	_____
11.	78.59	_____	_____	_____
12.	603.2	_____	_____	_____
13.	48.67	_____	_____	_____
14.	93.01	_____	_____	_____

Decimals: Multiplying

Name _____

Find each product.

Factor	.3	1 dec. place
Factor	× .9	1 dec. place
Product	.27	2 dec. places

1. Multiply as you would whole numbers.
2. The number of decimal places in the product is the sum of the decimal places in the factors.

TIP: *When the problem is presented horizontally (see the one below), make sure to line up the numbers on the right. Do not line up the decimal points.*

$$.23 \times 0.6$$

Correct	*Incorrect*
.23	.23
× 0.6	× 0.6

---

1. .2
   × 6

2. .6
   × .4

3. 4.23
   × 0.6

4. 1.37
   × 0.5

5. 3.76
   × 8

6. .41
   × .15

7. 6.5
   × .35

8. 6.4
   × 8.9

9. 5.32
   × .87

10. 28.6
    × .395

11. 7.23
    × .054

12. 28.6
    × 1.97

13. $6.8 \times 3.2 =$

14. $9.6 \times 0.56 =$

15. $0.356 \times 4.2 =$

16. $0.072 \times 6.2 =$

17. $5.65 \times 0.9 =$

18. $8.72 \times 91.3 =$

19. $16.1 \times 5.3 =$

20. $5.8 \times 1.6 =$

Decimals: More Multiplying

Name _____

Find each product.

0.05	**2 decimal places**
× 00.2	**1 decimal place**
10	
000	
.0010	**3 decimal places**

TIP: *You may have to add extra zeros on the left of your product to show the correct number of decimal places as was done in the example. (Drop any unnecessary zeros at the end: .001 = answer)*

---

1. 0.06
   × 0.3

2. 0.006
   × 0.4

3. 325
   × 0.0002

4. 0.63
   × 0.05

5. 4.3
   × 0.004

6. 0.016
   × 2.1

7. 0.005
   × 0.06

8. 0.013
   × 1.1

9. 0.0012
   × 5.4

10. 538
    × 0.01

11. 0.007
    × 0.07

12. 45.05
    × 0.08

13. 0.08×0.015

14. 0.25×0.054

15. $47.6 \times .042$

16. $312 \times .0624$

17. 0.205×8.67

18. 5.75×0.075

19. $800.6 \times .043$

20. $.0314 \times 26$

Decimals: Estimating Quotients

Name _____

Estimate each quotient. Use an appropriate strategy.

Estimate by rounding: $312.88 \div 4.8$

$$300 \div 5 = 60$$

Estimate by using compatible numbers: $461.76 \div 8.7$

$$450 \div 9 = 50$$

Use compatible numbers.

1. $265.98 \div 3 =$

2. $724.62 \div 8 =$

3. $478.34 \div 6 =$

4. $282.54 \div 4 =$

5. $322.37 \div 7.6 =$

6. $354.93 \div 5.7 =$

Estimate by rounding.

7. $14.86 \div 3.2 =$

8. $55.78 \div 9.7 =$

9. $524.61 \div 9.8 =$

10. $483.6 \div 62 =$

11. $44.987 \div 4.8 =$

12. $283.67 \div 6.8 =$

13. $398.3 \div 8.1 =$

14. $97.8 \div 10.9 =$

15. $310.15 \div 28.72 =$

Decimals: Dividing by 10, 100 & 1,000   Name _____

Study the examples below. Then, complete the chart.

	÷ 10	÷ 100	÷ 1000
16.34	**1.634**	**.1634**	**.01634**
Move the decimal point . . .	*once* to the left.	*twice* to the left.	*three* times to the left.

TIP: *Add zeros if necessary (see ÷ 1000 above).*

	÷ **10**	÷ **100**	÷ **1000**
1. 2,789.317	_____	_____	_____
2. 3,430.052	_____	_____	_____
3. 1,605.83	_____	_____	_____
4. 7,259.94	_____	_____	_____
5. 681.3	_____	_____	_____
6. 545.9	_____	_____	_____
7. 453.2	_____	_____	_____
8. 986.03	_____	_____	_____
9. 210.7	_____	_____	_____
10. 6.253	_____	_____	_____
11. 7.102	_____	_____	_____
12. 13	_____	_____	_____
13. 206	_____	_____	_____

Decimals: Dividing by Whole Numbers

Name _____

Find each quotient.

$$29.1 \div 5$$

$5\overline{)29.1}$ ← 1. Bring the decimal point up into the quotient.

$$
\begin{array}{r}
5.82 \\
5\overline{)29.10} \\
-25 \\
\hline
41 \\
-40 \\
\hline
10 \\
-10 \\
\hline
0 \\
\end{array}
$$
← 2. Divide. Add zeros if necessary.

---

1. $3\overline{)50.4}$

2. $6\overline{)53.58}$

3. $4\overline{)25.92}$

4. $9\overline{)5.166}$

5. $32\overline{)120.96}$

6. $57\overline{)202.35}$

7. $7\overline{)41.867}$

8. $21\overline{)92.001}$

9. $8\overline{)45.36}$

10. $62\overline{)269.70}$

11. $7\overline{)132.72}$

12. $51\overline{)348.84}$

13. $9\overline{)7.857}$

14. $22\overline{)0.726}$

15. $45\overline{)3262.5}$

16. $83\overline{)6.308}$

Decimals: Dividing by Decimals

Name _____

Find each quotient.

$$48 \div .6$$

$$6\overline{)48}$$

$$6\overline{)48.0}$$

$$\begin{array}{r} 80 \\ 6\overline{)480} \\ \underline{480} \\ 0 \end{array}$$

1. Change the divisor to a whole number by moving the decimal point to the right.
2. Move the decimal point in the dividend the same number of spaces. Add zeros if necessary.
3. Divide the same way as whole numbers. Remember: Bring the decimal point up in the quotient.

---

1. $.5\overline{)3.5}$

2. $1.6\overline{).768}$

3. $2.2\overline{)8.36}$

4. $.5\overline{)32.05}$

5. $3.1\overline{)19.84}$

6. $4.6\overline{)23.92}$

7. $.64\overline{)4.672}$

8. $.34\overline{).782}$

9. $7.2\overline{)117.36}$

10. $.81\overline{)1.701}$

11. $5.4\overline{)39.42}$

12. $.03\overline{).48}$

13. $1.24\overline{)76.88}$

14. $3.2\overline{)185.6}$

15. $.16\overline{)72}$

16. $.8\overline{)6.016}$

Decimals: Scientific Notation

Name _____

Part I. Write each number in scientific notation.

6,700,000.
$\underline{6.7} \times 10^{\underline{6}}$

1. Move the decimal point to change your number (n) so that $1 \leq n < 10$.

.00000023

$\underline{2.3} \times 10^{\underline{-7}}$

2. Count how many places you moved the decimal point. Place that number as your power of 10 (*positive* if you moved to the left, *negative* if you moved to the right).

---

3.   0.0004

1.   140,000   2.   64,900,000

6.   0.000015

4.   99,000,000   5.   350,000

9.   13,000,000,000

7.   0.00038   8.   7,200,000

12.   2,500,000

10.   0.000054   11.   0.00009

Part II. Write each number in standard form.

7.23×10^{4}
72,300

1. Look at the exponent on the 10.
2. If it is *positive*, move the decimal point that many places to the right.

3.5×10^{-5}
.000035

3. If it is *negative*, move it that many places to the left.

---

13. 1.03×10^{7} 14. 4.7×10^{-8} 15. 3.7×10^{-1}

16. 5.2×10^{10} 17. 4.698×10^{2} 18. 5.12×10^{-5}

19. 2.1×10^{6} 20. 6.8×10^{-4} 21. 7.6×10^{5}

Decimals: Problem Solving

Solve each problem.

1. Keri bought lunch for her and a friend.
   She ordered 2 hamburgers at $.99 each,
   2 fries at $.79 each, and 2 sodas at $.89.
   each. How much money did she spend on
   lunch?

2. Find the total cost of 4 movie tickets at
   $6.75 each.

3. The total rainfall in Seattle last July was
   1.86 inches. What was the average daily
   rainfall in that city in July?

4. If a class of 36 students share the cost of
   their class party, how much will each
   student pay if the total cost is $95.40?

5. How much change from $20 should you
   receive after purchasing 2 CD's that cost
   $8.99 each?

6. Tanner bought a package of 100 paper
   napkins for $1.79. How much was each
   napkin? Round to the nearest cent.

7. Bananas cost $0.39 per pound. Mandy
   bought 3 pounds. How much did Mandy
   pay for the bananas?

8. Michelle, a nurse, earns $566.35 per
   week. If she works 40 hours a week, how
   much does she earn per hour?

9. George, a musician, works 35 hours in a
   week. If he earns $18.15 per hour, how
   much does he earn each week?

1.
2.
3.
4.
5.
6.
7.
8.
9.

Number Theory: Exponents

$$3 \cdot 3 \cdot 3 \cdot 3 \cdot 3 = 3^5 \quad \nearrow exponent$$
$$\searrow base$$

An *exponent* tells the number of times a *base* is multiplied by itself.

$4^3 = \underline{4 \cdot 4 \cdot 4}$	Expanded form.
$2 \cdot 2 \cdot 2 \cdot 2 = \underline{2^4}$	Exponent form.
$5^2 = \underline{25}$	Simplified.

Write each problem in expanded form.

1. 6^2 2. 8^4 3. 2^5

4. 10^3 5. 7^6 6. 9^7

7. 3^2 8. 4^3 9. 5^4

Write in exponent form.

10. $3 \cdot 3 \cdot 3$ 11. $12 \cdot 12$ 12. $6 \cdot 6 \cdot 6 \cdot 6$

13. $5 \cdot 5$ 14. $7 \cdot 7 \cdot 7 \cdot 7 \cdot 7$ 15. $8 \cdot 8 \cdot 8$

16. $2 \cdot 2 \cdot 2 \cdot 2$ 17. $9 \cdot 9 \cdot 9$ 18. $10 \cdot 10 \cdot 10 \cdot 10$

Simplify.

19. 11^2 20. 5^3 21. 7^4

22. 3^3 23. 10^2 24. 9^5

Number Theory: Prime & Composite Numbers

Tell whether each number is prime (P) or composite (C).

A **prime** number is a number greater than one that has exactly two factors, 1 and itself. $3 = 1 \times 3$ $7 = 1 \times 7$

A **composite** number is a number greater than one that has more than two factors. $6 = 1 \times 6$ and 2×3 (4 factors)

---

1. 8

2. 10

3. 19

4. 20

5. 23

6. 9

7. 11

8. 15

9. 5

10. 16

11. 25

12. 29

13. 30

14. 21

15. 51

16. 17

17. 35

18. 27

19. 100

20. 99

21. 63

22. 70

23. 37

24. 44

25. 83

26. 13

27. 54

28. 67

 THINK ABOUT IT!

29. Consecutive primes, such as 11 and 13, that have a difference of 2, are called twin primes. Find three more pairs of twin primes.

Number Theory: Prime Factorization

Name _____

Draw a factor tree for each number. Then write the prime factorization. Use exponents when possible.

<u>Prime factorization</u> of a composite number is taking that number and expressing it as a product of all prime factors.

Factor tree:

Prime Factorization
$2 \cdot 2 \cdot 2 \cdot 5 = 2^3 \cdot 5$

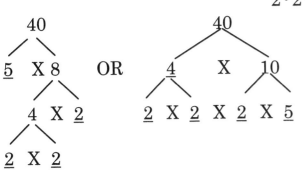

MATH FACTS
The famous artist, M.C. Escher, used math concepts to create bizarre, yet beautiful artistic images! His work is so detailed that it appears mind-boggling to people when they first look at it.

TIP: *Remember, the prime factorization must be written in order from smallest base up to largest base. $2^3 \cdot 5$, not $5 \cdot 2^3$*

---

1. 36

2. 84

3. 100

4. 64

5. 81

6. 144

7. 51

8. 240

Number Theory: Greatest Common Factor

Find the Greatest Common Factor (GCF) of each pair of numbers.

16, 24

16: 1×16, $2 \times$ ⑧
24: 1×24, 2×12, $3 \times$ ⑧, 4×6

GCF = 8

1. List all factors of each number.

2. Find the greatest factor common to both numbers.

---

1. 3, 12

2. 8, 24

3. 12, 16

4. 20, 28

5. 15, 21

6. 24, 40

7. 12, 20

8. 18, 27

9. 45, 60

10. 28, 42

11. 18, 45

12. 26, 52

13. 42, 56

14. 20, 36

15. 18, 72

Number Theory: Least Common Multiple Name _____

Find the Least Common Multiple (LCM) for each pair of numbers.

9, 12

1. List some multiples for each number.

9: 9, 18, 27, (36), 45
12: 12, 24, (36), 48, 60
LCM = 36

2. Find the smallest multiple common to both numbers.

1. 2, 4

2. 3, 6

3. 6, 8

4. 9, 6

5. 4, 10

6. 6, 4

7. 3, 5

8. 5, 10

9. 10, 12

10. 8, 10

11. 3, 12

12. 5, 6

13. 4, 16

14. 12, 18

15. 15, 20

Number Theory: Problem Solving

Solve each problem.

1. Lisa made a row of tiles that was 84 inches long. Barry's row was 96 inches long. What is the largest size tile they might have been using if all the tiles were the same size?

   1.

2. The sum of two numbers is 185. Their product is 900. What are the numbers?

   2.

3. A kangaroo and a rabbit start together and jump along the same path. The kangaroo always jumps 9 feet and the rabbit always jumps 4 feet. Will they ever land on the same spot again? Where?

   3.

4. Suppose the kangaroo jumps 8 feet each time and the rabbit jumps 6 feet. They will eventually land on 192 feet. Who will take more jumps to get there? How many more jumps will be taken?

   4.

5. Taylor's school band will march behind Richard's band in a parade. Each row of both marching bands must have the same number of students. The first band has 36 students, and the second one has 45. What is the greatest number of students that can be in each row?

   5.

6. Dorothy is arranging 36 chairs in the cafeteria for a concert. List all the ways she could arrange the chairs in equal rows.

   6.

Fractions: Equivalent Fractions

Name _____

Find the missing numerator or denominator to make equivalent fractions.

$\frac{2}{3} = \frac{}{6}$ Multiply the numerator and denominator by the same number. $\frac{2 \times 2}{3 \times 2} = \frac{\textcircled{4}}{6}$

---

1. $\frac{3}{4} = \frac{}{8}$

2. $\frac{2}{5} = \frac{}{10}$

3. $\frac{1}{2} = \frac{}{6}$

4. $\frac{5}{6} = \frac{}{12}$

5. $\frac{3}{7} = \frac{6}{}$

6. $\frac{5}{8} = \frac{}{24}$

7. $\frac{2}{3} = \frac{8}{}$

8. $\frac{8}{9} = \frac{}{36}$

9. $\frac{7}{8} = \frac{}{32}$

10. $\frac{4}{5} = \frac{}{20}$

11. $\frac{1}{10} = \frac{5}{}$

12. $\frac{3}{3} = \frac{}{15}$

13. $\frac{5}{12} = \frac{}{36}$

14. $\frac{2}{9} = \frac{10}{}$

15. $\frac{6}{11} = \frac{}{55}$

16. $\frac{9}{10} = \frac{45}{}$

17. $\frac{3}{4} = \frac{}{40}$

18. $\frac{5}{9} = \frac{20}{}$

19. $\frac{3}{8} = \frac{}{64}$

20. $\frac{9}{14} = \frac{27}{}$

21. $\frac{1}{15} = \frac{}{60}$

22. $\frac{2}{3} = \frac{}{36}$

23. $\frac{4}{4} = \frac{}{16}$

24. $\frac{6}{7} = \frac{}{42}$

 THINK ABOUT IT!

25. In one week it rained $\frac{3}{4}$ inch on Monday, $\frac{1}{3}$ inch on Tuesday, $\frac{6}{8}$ inch on Wednesday, and $\frac{1}{8}$ inch on Thursday. Which two days in that week had the same amount of rain?

Fractions: Reducing Fractions

Name _____

Reduce to lowest terms.

$$\frac{8}{24}$$ To reduce a fraction to lowest terms, divide its numerator and denominator by their GCF. $$\frac{8 \div 8}{24 \div 8} = \frac{1}{3}$$

TIP: *You know a fraction is in lowest terms when the GCF of its numerator and denominator is 1.*

---

1. $\dfrac{18}{24}$

2. $\dfrac{6}{30}$

3. $\dfrac{7}{35}$

4. $\dfrac{6}{12}$

5. $\dfrac{7}{8}$

6. $\dfrac{25}{30}$

7. $\dfrac{3}{6}$

8. $\dfrac{5}{15}$

9. $\dfrac{12}{16}$

10. $\dfrac{9}{24}$

11. $\dfrac{8}{15}$

12. $\dfrac{20}{30}$

13. $\dfrac{5}{10}$

14. $\dfrac{18}{20}$

15. $\dfrac{2}{15}$

16. $\dfrac{7}{21}$

17. $\dfrac{15}{60}$

18. $\dfrac{6}{8}$

19. $\dfrac{16}{20}$

20. $\dfrac{24}{32}$

21. $\dfrac{16}{32}$

22. $\dfrac{20}{45}$

23. $\dfrac{17}{51}$

24. $\dfrac{27}{36}$

 THINK ABOUT IT!

25. See how many numbers you can find to fill in $\Box$. $\dfrac{\Box}{18}$ Each number must be less than 18, and the fraction must be in lowest terms.

Fractions: Comparing and Ordering

Name _____

Part 1: Write <, >, or = for each

$\dfrac{2}{3}$ ◯ $\dfrac{5}{6}$ To compare two fractions find their cross products and compare.

$^{12}\dfrac{2}{3}$ ⨯ $\dfrac{5}{6}^{15}$ 12<15, so $\dfrac{2}{3}$ (<) $\dfrac{5}{6}$

---

1. $\dfrac{6}{10}$ ◯ $\dfrac{3}{5}$

2. $\dfrac{1}{3}$ ◯ $\dfrac{2}{4}$

3. $\dfrac{1}{3}$ ◯ $\dfrac{1}{4}$

4. $\dfrac{5}{8}$ ◯ $\dfrac{3}{4}$

5. $\dfrac{1}{4}$ ◯ $\dfrac{2}{10}$

6. $\dfrac{3}{9}$ ◯ $\dfrac{2}{8}$

7. $\dfrac{1}{2}$ ◯ $\dfrac{3}{8}$

8. $\dfrac{1}{3}$ ◯ $\dfrac{3}{5}$

9. $\dfrac{2}{3}$ ◯ $\dfrac{2}{5}$

10. $\dfrac{3}{4}$ ◯ $\dfrac{7}{10}$

11. $\dfrac{2}{10}$ ◯ $\dfrac{1}{6}$

12. $\dfrac{2}{3}$ ◯ $\dfrac{8}{12}$

13. $\dfrac{6}{15}$ ◯ $\dfrac{4}{10}$

14. $\dfrac{7}{12}$ ◯ $\dfrac{5}{6}$

15. $\dfrac{1}{3}$ ◯ $\dfrac{3}{8}$

Part II: Order from least to greatest

TIP: *Try changing the fractions to decimals, then compare them.*

16. $\dfrac{3}{4}$, $\dfrac{3}{8}$, $\dfrac{3}{7}$

17. $\dfrac{1}{3}$, $\dfrac{1}{4}$, $\dfrac{1}{5}$

18. $\dfrac{2}{5}$, $\dfrac{1}{4}$, $\dfrac{1}{2}$, $\dfrac{3}{5}$

19. $\dfrac{5}{6}$, $\dfrac{7}{9}$, $\dfrac{13}{18}$, $\dfrac{2}{3}$

20. $\dfrac{2}{9}$, $\dfrac{2}{5}$, $\dfrac{2}{7}$, $\dfrac{2}{3}$

21. $\dfrac{3}{4}$, $\dfrac{2}{3}$, $\dfrac{1}{2}$, $\dfrac{4}{5}$

Fractions: Improper Fractions & Mixed Numbers

Part I. Write each improper fraction as a mixed number or a whole number.

$$\frac{20}{6}$$

1. Divide the numerator by the denominator.

$$6\overline{)20}\;\;^{3}$$
$$\underline{-18}$$

2. If there is a remainder, put it in fraction form over the divisor.

3. Reduce fraction to lowest terms.

$$2 = 3\frac{2}{6} = 3\frac{1}{3}$$

1. $\frac{17}{5}$ 2. $\frac{14}{4}$ 3. $\frac{13}{2}$ 4. $\frac{20}{5}$ 5. $\frac{18}{4}$

6. $\frac{11}{5}$ 7. $\frac{40}{12}$ 8. $\frac{36}{6}$ 9. $\frac{9}{2}$ 10. $\frac{7}{3}$

11. $\frac{21}{4}$ 12. $\frac{6}{5}$ 13. $\frac{19}{3}$ 14. $\frac{4}{3}$ 15. $\frac{22}{4}$

Part II. Write each mixed number as an improper fraction.

$$4\frac{2}{3}$$

1. Multiply the whole number by the denominator.

$$4 \times 3 + 2 = \frac{14}{3}$$

2. Add the numerator.

3. Place that number over the denominator.

16. $3\frac{2}{3}$ 17. $6\frac{1}{4}$ 18. $2\frac{1}{8}$ 19. $5\frac{4}{5}$ 20. $1\frac{9}{10}$

21. $4\frac{3}{8}$ 22. $7\frac{2}{5}$ 23. $9\frac{2}{7}$ 24. $8\frac{3}{5}$ 25. $6\frac{4}{7}$

26. $2\frac{3}{7}$ 27. $5\frac{1}{9}$ 28. $4\frac{1}{2}$ 29. $3\frac{7}{8}$ 30. $7\frac{3}{4}$

Fractions: Fractions as Decimals

Name _____

Write each fraction as a decimal. Round to the nearest hundredth, if necessary.

$\frac{1}{2}$

$1 \div 2 = 0.5$

To change a fraction to a decimal, divide the numerator by the denominator.

---

1. $\frac{3}{4}$

2. $\frac{2}{5}$

3. $\frac{1}{4}$

4. $\frac{1}{6}$

5. $\frac{7}{8}$

6. $\frac{3}{7}$

7. $\frac{4}{5}$

8. $\frac{1}{3}$

9. $\frac{2}{10}$

10. $\frac{3}{5}$

11. $\frac{2}{3}$

12. $\frac{5}{6}$

13. $\frac{3}{8}$

14. $\frac{9}{10}$

15. $\frac{2}{9}$

16. $\frac{5}{8}$

17. $\frac{5}{16}$

18. $\frac{7}{2}$

19. $\frac{4}{9}$

20. $\frac{2}{15}$

21. $\frac{7}{20}$

22. $\frac{17}{6}$

23. $\frac{11}{6}$

24. $\frac{10}{13}$

25. $\frac{17}{100}$

26. $\frac{8}{5}$

27. $\frac{9}{16}$

28. $\frac{7}{15}$

29. $\frac{5}{9}$

30. $\frac{12}{25}$

31. $\frac{11}{40}$

32. $\frac{21}{30}$

Fractions: Adding and Subtracting

• Fractions and Mixed Numbers with Common Denominators

Find each sum or difference. Reduce.

$$2\frac{1}{8}$$
$$+\ 4\frac{3}{8}$$
$$\overline{6\frac{4}{8} = 6\frac{1}{2}}$$

1. Add or subtract the whole numbers if there are any.

2. Add or subtract the numerators of the fractions. Place over their common denominator.

3. Reduce if necessary.

---

1. $\dfrac{2}{11}$
$+\ \dfrac{3}{11}$

2. $\dfrac{2}{5}$
$+\ \dfrac{2}{5}$

3. $\dfrac{9}{8}$
$-\ \dfrac{3}{8}$

4. $\dfrac{1}{6}$
$+\ \dfrac{5}{6}$

5. $\dfrac{3}{4}$
$-\ \dfrac{3}{4}$

6. $\dfrac{11}{12}$
$-\ \dfrac{5}{12}$

7. $\dfrac{7}{8}$
$+\ \dfrac{4}{8}$

8. $\dfrac{4}{6}$
$-\ \dfrac{1}{6}$

9. $\dfrac{19}{20}$
$-\ \dfrac{13}{20}$

10. $\dfrac{14}{24}$
$+\ \dfrac{10}{24}$

11. $3\dfrac{1}{8}$
$+\ 4\dfrac{4}{8}$

12. $7\dfrac{5}{6}$
$-\ 2\dfrac{3}{6}$

13. $7\dfrac{1}{6}$
$+\ 3\dfrac{3}{6}$

14. $19\dfrac{7}{8}$
$-\ 12\dfrac{7}{8}$

15. $21\dfrac{1}{4}$
$+\ 14$

16. 6
$-\ 2\dfrac{5}{10}$

Fractions: Adding and Subtracting

Name _____

• Fractions with Unlike Denominators

Find each sum or difference. Reduce.

$$\frac{1}{3} \times \frac{4}{4} = \frac{4}{12}$$
$$+\frac{1}{4} \times \frac{3}{3} = \frac{3}{12}$$
$$\frac{7}{12}$$

1. Find the least common denominator (LCD), also known as the LCM, of both denominators.
2. Write equivalent fractions using the LCD.
3. Add or subtract the fractions, and reduce if necessary.

---

1. $\frac{7}{8}$
    $-\frac{1}{4}$

2. $\frac{1}{4}$
    $+\frac{5}{6}$

3. $\frac{1}{3}$
    $-\frac{2}{7}$

4. $\frac{4}{5}$
    $+\frac{3}{4}$

5. $\frac{1}{2}$
    $-\frac{1}{10}$

6. $\frac{2}{5}$
    $+\frac{2}{3}$

7. $\frac{3}{2}$
    $-\frac{1}{4}$

8. $\frac{5}{6}$
    $+\frac{1}{3}$

9. $\frac{7}{8}$
    $+\frac{3}{4}$

10. $\frac{5}{6}$
    $-\frac{1}{4}$

11. $\frac{1}{3}$
    $+\frac{7}{8}$

12. $\frac{3}{10}$
    $+\frac{2}{5}$

13. $\frac{5}{6}$
    $-\frac{5}{9}$

14. $\frac{2}{5}$
    $+\frac{1}{4}$

15. $\frac{9}{10}$
    $+\frac{5}{8}$

16. $\frac{2}{9}$
    $-\frac{1}{6}$

THINK ABOUT IT!

17. Without adding, tell whether the answer is **more** than one or **less** than one.

   a. $\frac{5}{8} + \frac{1}{2}$ b. $\frac{3}{4} + \frac{1}{2}$ c. $\frac{2}{5} + \frac{3}{8}$

Fractions: Adding and Subtracting   Name _____

• Mixed Numbers with Unlike Denominators

Find each sum or difference. Reduce.

$$8\frac{1}{5} = 8\frac{4}{20} = 7\frac{24}{20}$$
$$-2\frac{1}{4} = 2\frac{5}{20} = 2\frac{5}{20}$$
$$\overline{\hspace{3cm}} \quad \overline{\hspace{1.5cm}} \quad 5\frac{19}{20}$$

1. Find the least common denominator (LCD).
2. Write the equivalent fractions using the LCD.
3. Rename if necessary.
4. Add or subtract the whole numbers and fractions. Reduce if necessary.

---

1. $2\frac{2}{3}$
   $+ 12\frac{1}{2}$

2. $9\frac{3}{4}$
   $- 1\frac{1}{6}$

3. $2\frac{1}{2}$
   $+ 4\frac{3}{4}$

4. $14\frac{3}{8}$
   $- 5\frac{3}{4}$

5. $1\frac{1}{2}$
   $+ 4\frac{7}{8}$

6. $12\frac{1}{2}$
   $- 3\frac{3}{4}$

7. $8\frac{1}{2}$
   $+ 3\frac{5}{6}$

8. $5\frac{7}{10}$
   $- 2\frac{3}{5}$

9. $7\frac{1}{6}$
   $+ 3\frac{1}{4}$

10. $7\frac{1}{4}$
    $- 6\frac{5}{6}$

11. $6\frac{2}{3}$
    $+ 5\frac{1}{6}$

12. $6\frac{1}{2}$
    $- 5\frac{1}{3}$

13. $6\frac{1}{4} + 8\frac{1}{8} + 3\frac{1}{2} =$

14. $14 - 9\frac{7}{10} =$

15. $9\frac{1}{4} + 7\frac{7}{10} + 16\frac{1}{5} =$

16. $4\frac{2}{3} + 2\frac{1}{6} + 4\frac{1}{3} =$

17. $7\frac{3}{5} - 2\frac{9}{10} =$

18. $8\frac{1}{4} - 1\frac{3}{4} =$

Fractions: Problem Solving

Name _____

Solve each problem.

1. A literary magazine has 16 pages; $5\frac{1}{2}$ pages are short stories, and $6\frac{1}{2}$ pages are poems. How many pages are not short stories or poems?

2. Tom walked $\frac{1}{4}$ of a mile, then he started running. In all, he walked and ran $\frac{3}{4}$ of a mile. How far did he run?

3. James lives 7/10 of a mile from school. Billy lives 4/10 of a mile from school. Who lives closer? By how much?

4. Michele made a book from cardboard for her project. The cover was $13\frac{1}{2}$ inches long and $9\frac{3}{4}$ inches wide. How much longer was the cover than it was wide?

5. Grayson spent his first week of school doing $4\frac{3}{4}$ hours of homework. His sister Denise spent $6\frac{1}{2}$ hours doing her homework. How much longer did Denise spend doing homework than Grayson?

6. Jennifer wants to buy some ribbon to make bookmarks. She wants to make one bookmark 6 1/8 inches long and the other 9 13/16 inches long. How long will both ribbons be?

7. A recipe calls for $2\frac{1}{2}$ cups of white flour and $3\frac{3}{4}$ cups of rye flour. Can a person use a $1\frac{1}{2}$ quart (6 cup) mixing bowl to make the recipe? Explain your answer.

1.

2.

3.

4.

5.

6.

7.

Fractions: Multiplying Fractions and Mixed Numbers

Find each product. Reduce.

$1\frac{2}{3} \times 6 =$

$\frac{5}{3} \times \frac{6}{1} = \frac{10}{1} = 10$

1. Change each mixed number to an improper fraction.
2. Multiply the numerators.
3. Multiply the denominators.
4. Reduce if possible.

TIP: *You can reduce first by dividing a numerator and denominator by a common factor. This is called cross cancellation.*

---

1. $\frac{1}{4} \times \frac{1}{2}$

2. $2\frac{3}{4} \times 3\frac{2}{3}$

3. $\frac{1}{6} \times \frac{2}{5}$

4. $1\frac{2}{3} \times 9$

5. $\frac{3}{5} \times \frac{2}{3}$

6. $3\frac{4}{5} \times 2\frac{3}{4}$

7. $8 \times \frac{5}{12}$

8. $4 \times 3\frac{5}{8}$

9. $\frac{6}{15} \times \frac{3}{4}$

10. $2\frac{1}{10} \times 3\frac{3}{4}$

11. $\frac{5}{6} \times \frac{3}{4}$

12. $3\frac{1}{3} \times \frac{9}{10}$

13. $\frac{4}{9} \times \frac{3}{8}$

14. $5\frac{3}{4} \times 3\frac{1}{3}$

15. $2\frac{1}{2} \times \frac{4}{3}$

16. $2\frac{2}{3} \times 3\frac{1}{2}$

17. $4 \times \frac{7}{8}$

18. $3\frac{1}{10} \times 15$

19. $\frac{6}{7} \times \frac{1}{4}$

20. $7\frac{2}{3} \times 3\frac{1}{2}$

 THINK ABOUT IT!

21. If the product of two different numbers equals 1, then one of the numbers is greater than one and the other number is _____. Give an example to support your answer.

Fractions: Dividing Fractions and Mixed Numbers

Find each quotient. Reduce.

$$2\frac{9}{10} \div 3\frac{1}{2}$$

$$\frac{29}{10} \div \frac{7}{2}$$

$$\frac{29}{10} \times \frac{2}{7} = \frac{29}{35}$$

1. Write the mixed numbers (or whole numbers) as improper fractions.
2. To divide fractions, flip the second one and then multiply.
3. Reduce.

MATH FACTS

Have you ever wondered how much you'd weigh on the Moon, or Mars? With math knowledge, you can. In fact, with math you can figure out how much you'd weigh on Saturn's rings, assuming you could stand on them, of course.

TIP: *Remember that a whole number can be written as a fraction by placing it over one.* $6 = \dfrac{6}{1}$

---

1. $\dfrac{3}{4} \div \dfrac{1}{10}$

2. $3\dfrac{3}{5} \div 1\dfrac{1}{2}$

3. $15 \div \dfrac{3}{4}$

4. $2\dfrac{1}{2} \div 1\dfrac{1}{3}$

5. $4 \div \dfrac{3}{8}$

6. $\dfrac{5}{12} \div 4\dfrac{3}{8}$

7. $\dfrac{2}{3} \div \dfrac{3}{4}$

8. $3\dfrac{1}{2} \div 2\dfrac{1}{3}$

9. $\dfrac{1}{2} \div \dfrac{1}{4}$

10. $5\dfrac{1}{4} \div 2\dfrac{1}{2}$

11. $\dfrac{1}{3} \div \dfrac{2}{3}$

12. $1\dfrac{3}{8} \div 4\dfrac{1}{3}$

13. $\dfrac{7}{8} \div \dfrac{3}{4}$

14. $2\dfrac{1}{10} \div 1\dfrac{1}{5}$

15. $\dfrac{5}{6} \div \dfrac{5}{8}$

16. $10 \div 1\dfrac{1}{4}$

17. $5 \div \dfrac{1}{2}$

18. $4\dfrac{3}{5} \div 2\dfrac{1}{5}$

Fractions: Problem Solving

Solve each problem.

1. Karen was taking piano lessons. She was required to practice ¾ hour each night after dinner. How many minutes is that?

2. During a 60-minute television show, one advertiser has 2½ minutes of commercial time. Each commercial is ½ minute long. How many commercials does the advertiser have during the show?

3. Scott is going to plant bushes 3½ feet high along his fence. The fence is 1½ times as high as the bushes. What is the height of the fence?

4. Coach Starks' basketball team practices are ¾ hour long. The team spends 1/3 of that time exercising. How much of the practice time does the team exercise?

5. Ms. Reynolds has packed some training manuals for shipment. Each manual weighs 2½ pounds. The total weight of the box is 58¾ pounds. About how many manuals are in the box?

6. Mrs. Harrington is going out of town for 5½ days. Her 2 neighbors will watch the dog while she is away. They will divide the time equally. How long will each watch the dog?

7. Will and John spend 4½ hours cycling each week. How many hours do they spend cycling in 4 weeks?

1.

2.

3.

4.

5.

6.

7.

Ratio and Proportion: Writing Ratios

Name _____

A ratio compares two quantities and can be written as follows:

3 bananas to 4 apples

$\frac{3}{4}$ or 3:4 or 3 to 4

Write each ratio three different ways.

---

1. 5 tapes to 6 CD's

2. 30 country tapes to 40 classical tapes

3. 2 keyboards to 3 guitars

4. 7 comedies to 8 dramas

5. 6 apples to 11 oranges

6. 23 grapes to 41 raisins

7. 2 oranges to 5 bananas

8. 9 peaches to 10 plums

9. 12 girls to 25 students

10. 13 boys to 25 students

11. 1 teacher to 28 students

12. 3 administrators to 45 students

13. 3 giraffes to 5 gorillas

14. 12 flamingos to 4 parrots

15. 2 tigers to 3 lions

16. 9 monkeys to 4 apes

 THINK ABOUT IT!

17. The ratio of boys to all students in the school is 467:908. Are there more boys or more girls in the school?

Ratio and Proportion: Equal Ratios

Name _____

Determine whether each pair of ratios is equal. Write yes or no.

$$\overset{18}{}\overset{16}{}$$
$$\frac{6}{8} \times \frac{2}{3}$$
(no)

1. Cross multiply.
2. If the cross products are equal, the ratios are equal.

1. $\frac{9}{12}$, $\frac{24}{32}$

2. $\frac{42}{56}$, $\frac{7}{8}$

3. $\frac{56}{59}$, $\frac{34}{36}$

4. $\frac{4}{5}$, $\frac{28}{35}$

5. $\frac{3}{8}$, $\frac{12}{32}$

6. $\frac{6}{9}$, $\frac{8}{12}$

7. $\frac{7}{5}$, $\frac{6}{4}$

8. $\frac{8}{20}$, $\frac{6}{15}$

9. $\frac{12}{30}$, $\frac{3}{8}$

10. $\frac{5}{7}$, $\frac{3}{4}$

11. $\frac{2}{11}$, $\frac{6}{33}$

12. $\frac{2}{5}$, $\frac{6}{15}$

13. $\frac{14}{35}$, $\frac{16}{40}$

14. $\frac{2}{5}$, $\frac{10}{25}$

15. $\frac{6}{14}$, $\frac{3}{8}$

16. $\frac{15}{20}$, $\frac{36}{48}$

17. $\frac{24}{32}$, $\frac{45}{72}$

18. $\frac{20}{32}$, $\frac{35}{56}$

19. $\frac{5}{9}$, $\frac{18}{27}$

20. $\frac{75}{120}$, $\frac{40}{90}$

21. $\frac{8}{10}$, $\frac{20}{25}$

22. $\frac{12}{15}$, $\frac{16}{20}$

23. $\frac{5}{4}$, $\frac{15}{10}$

24. $\frac{4}{5}$, $\frac{20}{25}$

Ratio & Proportion: Solving Proportions   Name _____

Solve each proportion.

$$\frac{3}{4} = \frac{n}{32}$$

A proportion is two equal ratios. To solve:
   1. Find the cross products.

$$4 \times n = 3 \times 32$$
$$n = 96 \div 4$$
$$n = 24$$

   2. Division undoes multiplication to solve for n.

---

1. $\dfrac{4}{5} = \dfrac{n}{60}$

2. $\dfrac{3}{4} = \dfrac{n}{100}$

3. $\dfrac{1}{2} = \dfrac{n}{20}$

4. $\dfrac{2}{5} = \dfrac{n}{35}$

5. $\dfrac{2}{8} = \dfrac{n}{80}$

6. $\dfrac{4}{5} = \dfrac{n}{75}$

7. $\dfrac{3}{10} = \dfrac{n}{60}$

8. $\dfrac{3}{5} = \dfrac{n}{35}$

9. $\dfrac{1}{4} = \dfrac{n}{32}$

10. $\dfrac{4}{8} = \dfrac{n}{100}$

11. $\dfrac{4}{5} = \dfrac{n}{45}$

12. $\dfrac{1}{8} = \dfrac{n}{48}$

13. $\dfrac{1}{2} = \dfrac{n}{16}$

14. $\dfrac{3}{2} = \dfrac{n}{50}$

15. $\dfrac{3}{8} = \dfrac{n}{56}$

16. $\dfrac{7}{12} = \dfrac{n}{120}$

17. $\dfrac{7}{5} = \dfrac{n}{60}$

18. $\dfrac{5}{8} = \dfrac{n}{64}$

19. $\dfrac{5}{6} = \dfrac{n}{66}$

20. $\dfrac{5}{8} = \dfrac{n}{32}$

21. $\dfrac{4}{3} = \dfrac{n}{45}$

22. $\dfrac{7}{8} = \dfrac{n}{72}$

23. $\dfrac{7}{3} = \dfrac{n}{21}$

24. $\dfrac{9}{6} = \dfrac{n}{4}$

 THINK ABOUT IT!

25. Without solving, tell whether <u>n</u> is more than or less than 50.

A. $\dfrac{6}{15} = \dfrac{n}{100}$

B. $\dfrac{22}{40} = \dfrac{n}{100}$

C. $\dfrac{12}{25} = \dfrac{n}{100}$

Ratio and Proportion: Problem Solving

Name _____

For each problem, write a proportion and then solve.

1. There are 2 students in the drama club for every 3 students in the chorus. If there are 24 students in the chorus, how many are in the drama club?

2. For the class field trip, there must be 12 chaperones for every 100 students. How many chaperones will be needed for 150 students?

3. During the season, Juan batted 96 times and got 36 hits. Carlos batted 72 times and had the same ratio of hits to bats as Juan. How many hits did Carlos get?

4. On Martin's bike, the rear wheel turns 588 times per mile. If the ratio of pedal turns to rear wheel turns in fourth gear is 6 to 14, how many times will he have to turn the pedals to ride one mile?

5. In Tanner's neighborhood, the ratio of dogs to cats is 3 to 4. There are 28 cats. How many dogs are there?

6. K'Lee wants to make a beef stew for her 12 dinner guests. The recipe she has serves 8 and calls for 4 pounds of beef. How much beef should K'Lee use?

7. Stan's 12-foot boat can travel 7 miles in 2 hours when he is fishing. How far can Stan travel in 5 hours?

1. _____

2. _____

3. _____

4. _____

5. _____

6. _____

7. _____

Percent: Understanding Percent

Name _____

Part I: Write each ratio as a percent.

43:100 = 43%   A percent is a special ratio
that compares a quantity to 100.

$\frac{61}{100} = 61\%$

1. 19:100

2. $\frac{41}{100}$

3. $\frac{13}{100}$

4. 29:100

5. 57 to 100

6. 91:100

7. 17 to 100

8. $\frac{83}{100}$

9. 64 to 100

10. 73:100

11. $\frac{51}{100}$

12. 65:100

Part II: Write each percent as a ratio (use fractions in lowest terms).

13. 2%

14. 44%

15. 18%

16. 50%

17. 91%

18. 73%

19. 84%

20. 20%

21. 65%

22. 33%

23. 25%

24. 10%

25. 95%

26. 45%

27. 70%

28. 86%

 THINK ABOUT IT!

29. A sports writer for the Daily Chronicle
writes that a player "gave a 110% effort."
What do you think the writer meant?

MATH FACTS

Computers and video games are
built on the language of math. The
most-exciting games, and the
programs you use to "surf the net" are
created from algebraic logic and binary
numbers of "1's" and "0's."
Computers use numbers to build
everything you see!

Percent: Writing Decimals as Percents   Name _____

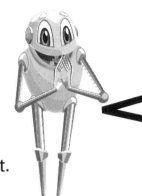

Write each decimal as a percent.

$0.62 \times 100 =$
62%

To change a decimal to a percent, multiply by 100 and add the percent sign.

TIP: *When you multiply by 100, it moves the decimal point two places to the right. Simply moving the decimal point two places to the right changes the decimal to a percent.*

---

1. 0.09   2. 0.21   3. 0.38   4. 0.79

5. 0.65   6. 0.56   7. 0.44   8. 0.03

9. 0.99   10. 0.87   11. 0.61   12. 0.33

13. 0.82   14. 0.53   15. 0.06   16. 0.2

17. 0.01   18. 0.47   19. 0.58   20. 0.34

21. 0.25   22. 0.73   23. 0.6   24. 0.15

25. 0.27   26. 0.84   27. 0.93   28. 0.41

Percents: Writing Fractions as Percents   Name _____

Write each fraction as a percent.

$\dfrac{10}{15}$

$10 \div 15 = .67$

67%

1. Change the fraction to a decimal and round to the nearest hundredth. (numerator ÷ denominator)
2. Change the decimal to a percent (move the decimal two places to the right and add a percent sign).

TIP: *A percent compares a quantity to 100. If the fraction's denominator is out of 100, then your numerator is the percent.* $\dfrac{52}{100} = 52\%$

1. $\dfrac{3}{4}$

2. $\dfrac{1}{5}$

3. $\dfrac{3}{8}$

4. $\dfrac{2}{5}$

5. $\dfrac{6}{10}$

6. $\dfrac{11}{20}$

7. $\dfrac{23}{40}$

8. $\dfrac{11}{15}$

9. $\dfrac{1}{2}$

10. $\dfrac{7}{10}$

11. $\dfrac{17}{20}$

12. $\dfrac{23}{30}$

13. $\dfrac{64}{100}$

14. $\dfrac{50}{70}$

15. $\dfrac{19}{25}$

16. $\dfrac{25}{40}$

17. $\dfrac{18}{50}$

18. $\dfrac{21}{60}$

19. $\dfrac{3}{5}$

20. $\dfrac{15}{40}$

21. $\dfrac{19}{20}$

22. $\dfrac{5}{6}$

23. $\dfrac{4}{5}$

24. $\dfrac{1}{3}$

25. $\dfrac{31}{50}$

26. $\dfrac{76}{100}$

27. $\dfrac{16}{30}$

28. $\dfrac{51}{52}$

Percents: Percents, Fractions & Decimals Name _____

Part I: Write each percent as a decimal.

42%
0.42

To change a percent to a decimal, move the decimal point two places to the left.
6% = 0.06   20% = 0.2

1. 51%

2. 28%

3. 9%

4. 30%

5. 16%

6. 73%

7. 64%

8. 82%

9. 55%

10. 96%

11. 210%

12. 48%

Part II: Write each percent as a fraction in lowest terms.

$$65\% = \frac{65}{100} = \frac{13}{20}$$

1. Drop the percent sign and place the number over 100.
2. Reduce to lowest terms.

13. 50%

14. 25%

15. 3%

16. 80%

17. 95%

18. 61%

19. 42%

20. 33%

21. 73%

22. 38%

23. 84%

24. 67%

 THINK ABOUT IT!

25. Place the following in order from the smallest to the largest.

27%, $\frac{74}{100}$,   0.45,   90%, $\frac{1}{2}$,   0.6

Percents: Percent of a Number

Name _____

Find the percent of each number.

Method I Use fractions 75% of 84 $\frac{3}{4} \times 84$ $\boxed{63}$		**Method II** Use decimals 42% of 90 $.42 \times 90$ $\boxed{37.8}$

---

1. 50% of 48

2. 10% of 35

3. 25% of 32

4. 94% of 64

5. 64% of 50

6. 72% of 15

7. 18% of 25

8. 24% of 30

9. 11% of 20

10. 3% of 32

11. 24% of 36

12. 76% of 95

13. 43% of 85

14. 19% of 26

15. 87% of 24

16. 40% of 40

17. 25% of 52

18. 90% of 80

19. 10% of 250

20. 50% of 98

21. 67% of 320

 THINK ABOUT IT!

22. Write each percent without multiplying. $\boxed{26 \times 42 = 1,092}$
    a. 42% of 26   b. 26% of 42   c. 26% of 420

Percents: Problem Solving

Name _____

Solve each problem. Round the answers.

1. Barry is in a class of 12 boys and 11 girls. 35% of the class walk to school. How many students walk to school?

1.

2. In Cheryl's class, 5 students wear glasses (including Cheryl). The other 21 students do not wear glasses. What percent of the students wear glasses? What percent don't wear any glasses?

2.

3. Kimberly asked 50 students what their favorite food was. 36% chose pizza and $\frac{1}{4}$ chose spaghetti. What percentage of the students chose a food other than pizza and spaghetti?

3.

4. In Iris' class, 5 students are in chorus, 6 are in band and 4 are in orchestra. If there are 24 students in Iris' class, what percent are in the chorus, band, and orchestra?

4.

5. Bunche Middle School's annual charity drive has a goal of raising $5,000. In 3 weeks, it raised 3/5 of its goal. The next week the school raised $450. How much money was still needed to be raised to meet the $5,000 goal?

5.

6. Beth's goal was to raise $250 during her summer vacation. During the first month she raised 60%. How much did Beth raise? How much more money did she need to meet her goal?

6.

Geometry: Classifying Angles

Name _____

Classify each angle as acute, right, obtuse, or straight.

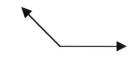 Acute Angle
< 90°

Right Angle
= 90°

Obtuse Angle
90° < x < 180°

Straight Angle
= 180°

1. _____

2. _____

3. _____

4. _____

5. _____

6. _____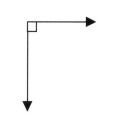

7. _____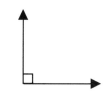

8. _____

9. _____

10. _____

11. _____

12. _____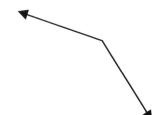

THINK ABOUT IT!

A.

B.

13. Janet thinks angle A is greater than angle B. Her classmate Linda thinks they're the same size. What do you think? Do the length of the rays have anything to do with the measure of the angles?

Geometry: Classifying Quadrilaterals

Name _____

Classify each quadrilateral as a square, rectangle, parallelogram, trapezoid or rhombus.

Square
All sides equal
All angles 90°
Parallelogram
Opposite sides
parallel

Rectangle
Opposite sides equal
All angles 90°
Trapezoid
1 pair of parallel sides

Rhombus
All sides equal

TIP: *Some quadrilaterals can be classified by two different names. For example, a rectangle is also a parallelogram.*

1.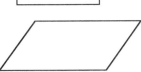

2.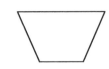

3.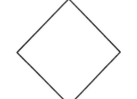

4.

5.

6.

7.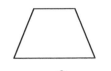

8.

9.

10.

11.

12.

Geometry: Classifying Triangles

Name _____

Classify each triangle by its sides and angles.

By sides:

Equilateral

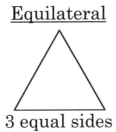

3 equal sides

Isosceles

2 equal sides

Scalene

no equal sides

By angles:

Acute

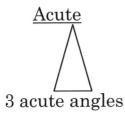

3 acute angles

Obtuse

1 obtuse angle

Right

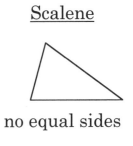

1 right angle

1.

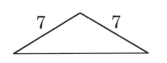

2.

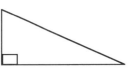

3.

4.

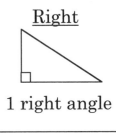

5.

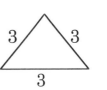

6.

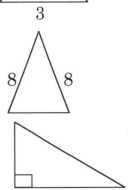

7.

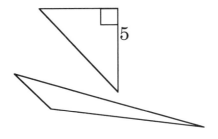

8.

9.

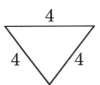

10.

Geometry: Symmetry

Draw all lines of symmetry in each figure. If the figure has none, write "none."

A line of symmetry cuts a figure in half so that you see the exact same image on each side of the line.

1.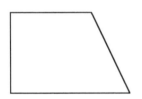

2.

3.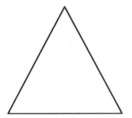

4.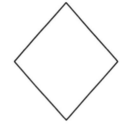

5.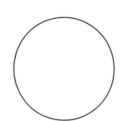

6.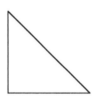

7.

8.

9.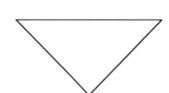

10.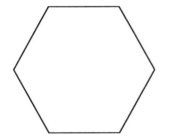

11.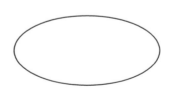

12.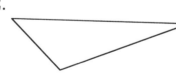

Geometry: Congruent & Similar Figures Name _____

Tell whether each pair of figures is similar, congruent or neither.

Two figures are _similar_ if they have the same shape but are a different size.

Two figures are _congruent_ if they have the same size and shape.

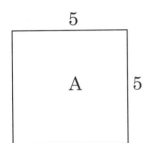 A 5 5

B 5 5 ⟶ Congruent

TIP: _To test whether two figures are similar, you should be able to make a proportion using the lengths of matching sides._

1.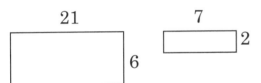

4.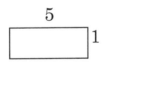

2.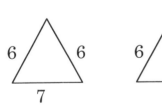

5.

3.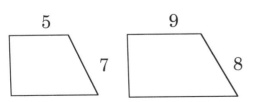

6.

69

Measurement: Customary System

Name _____

Study the charts below. Then, complete the problems.

Length	*Weight*	*Capacity*
12 in. = 1 ft	16 oz. = 1 lb	8 fl. oz. = 1 c
3 ft. = 1 yd	2,000 lbs. = 1 T	2 c. = 1 pt
5,280 ft. = 1 mi		2 pt. = 1 qt
		4 qt. = 1 gal

TIP: *When going from a larger unit to a smaller one, multiply. (Example: gallons to cups) When going from a smaller unit to a larger one, divide. (Example: feet to yards)*

1. 99 ft = _____ yd

2. 9 gal = _____ qt

3. 9 qt = _____ pt

4. 5 T = _____ lb

5. 120 ft = _____ yd

6. 2 mi = _____ ft

7. 10 c = _____ pt

8. 3 gal = _____ pt

9. 5 yd = _____ ft

10. 5 yd = _____ in

11. 48 oz = _____ lb

12. 2 c = _____ fl. oz

13. 6,000 lb = _____ T

14. 8 qt = _____ gal

15. 10 ft = _____ in

16. 4 pt = _____ c

17. 36 in = _____ ft

18. 2 qt = _____ c

19. $2\frac{1}{2}$ T = _____ lb

20. 4 lb = _____ oz

21. 6 pt = _____ qt

22. 9 gal = _____ qt

23. 12 yd = _____ in

24. 4 c = _____ fl oz

Measurement: Computing Customary Units

Name _____

Find each sum, difference, or product.

```
   4 lb   7 oz  →  trade 1 lb     3 lb   23 oz        7 ft   9 in
 - 2 lb  12 oz      for 16 oz    - 2 lb   12 oz      +3 ft   8 in
                                  1 lb   11 oz       10 ft 17 in → rewrite as 11 ft   5 in
```

```
1.  6 lb     8 oz                    2.  10 ft      4 in
  - 2 lb     4 oz                      +3 ft        7 in
```

```
3.  6 ft    10 in                    4.  1 lb      9 oz
  - 5 ft     5 in                      ×           4
```

```
5.  8 lb     4 oz                    6.  3 lb      5 oz
  - 5 lb    10 oz                      ×            3
```

```
7.  11 ft    9 in                    8.  6 ft     11 in
  - 10 ft    5 in                      +3 ft       4 in
```

```
9.  2 ft     3 in                    10.  5 lb     8 oz
  ×          6                          +          10 oz
```

```
11.  8 ft    6 in                    12.  5 ft     3 in
   +7 ft     6 in                       - 1 ft     4 in
```

```
13.  4 ft    3 in                    14.  7 lb     0 oz
   ×         6                          - 3 lb     9 oz
```

```
15.  2 lb    3 oz                    16.  4 ft     0 in
   +1 lb    15 oz                       - 2 ft     5 in
```

```
17.  5 ft    4 in                    18.  8 ft     2 in
   +3 ft    11 in                       ×          5
```

Measurement: The Metric System

Name _____

Study the chart below, then complete each sentence.

$$\times 10 \quad\quad \times 10 \quad \times 10 \quad \times 10 \quad \times 10 \quad \times 10$$

			meter			
kilo-	hecto-	deka-	**_liter_**	deci-	centi-	milli-

$$\div 10 \quad\quad \div 10 \quad\quad \div 10 \quad \textbf{\textit{gram}} \div 10 \quad\quad \div 10 \quad \div 10$$

3.6 m = <u>360</u> cm
3.6 x 10^2 = 360

20 cm = <u>.0002</u> km
20 ÷ 10^5 = .0002

---

1. 3.54 m = _____ cm

2. 542 mg = _____ g

3. 4.332 L = _____ mL

4. 9.47 m = _____ cm

5. 39 cm = _____ m

6. 4.85 m = _____ mm

7. 46 mL = _____ L

8. 0.75 m = _____ cm

9. 256 cm = _____ m

10. 7.04 g = _____ cg

11. 6,367 mm = _____ m

12. 13.3 m = _____ cm

13. 19 km = _____ m

14. 6.5 g = _____ mg

15. 0.32 kg = _____ g

16. 1,264 L = _____ kL

17. 736 m = _____ km

18. 18.5 cm = _____ km

19. .022 kg = _____ mg

20. 12 g = _____ kg

21. 140 cm = _____ km

22. 7 m = _____ km

23. 22 cm = _____ m

24. .05 kg = _____ g

Measurement: Problem Solving

Name _____

Solve each problem.

1. Suppose a football field is 120 yards long and 53 yards, 1 foot wide. Calculate how much longer the length is than the width.

2. In checking the equipment for a game, the referee measured the air pressure of the football at 9.5 lbs. An approved football must have more than 12.5 lbs. and less than 13.5 lbs. of air pressure. How many pounds should be added to the football to bring the air pressure up to the minimum amount?

3. Karen has a board that is 4 ft., $2\frac{1}{2}$ in. long. She needs a piece for her bookshelf that measures 3 ft., $6\frac{1}{4}$ in. long. How much should she cut off her board to have what she needs?

4. A jar of applesauce holds 860 grams. How many milligrams is that?

5. To be prepared for the heat, a hiker carries 4,565 mL of water. How many liters of water does the hiker have?

6. A camel can carry a load of approximately 435,000 g. How many kilograms is that? How many milligrams?

7. A box of math textbooks weighs about 50 pounds. How many ounces is that?

8. If you drank 6 liters of milk a week, how many milliliters would that be each week?

1. _____

2. _____

3. _____

4. _____

5. _____

6. _____

7. _____

8. _____

Measurement: Perimeter & Area of Quadrilaterals

Find the perimeter and area of each quadrilateral.

Perimeter: distance around a figure

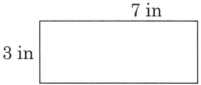

7 in

3 in

P = 2 x 3 + 2 x 7 = 20 in

Area: measure of what's inside

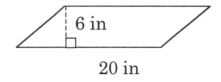

6 in

20 in

A= b x h
  = 20 x 6
  = 120 in²

---

1.   5 m

P=
A=

5 m

2.   10 m

P=
A=

4 m

3.

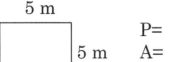

10 cm   12 cm   P=
   30 cm   A=

4.

6 cm

6 cm

P=
A=

5.   20 m

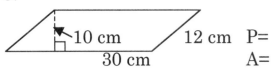

16 m / 18 m

P=
A=

6.

20 yd   P=
               A=

4 yd

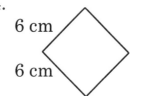

7.   9 ft

9 ft

P=
A=

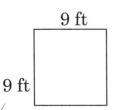

8.

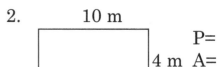

15 ft   A=
P=

10 ft   40 ft

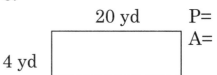

THINK ABOUT IT!

9. Look at the figure. Suppose the length of side B is doubled. What will happen to the area? Suppose it is tripled? Give examples to support your answer.

A

B

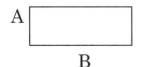

Measurement: Perimeter & Area of Triangles

Find the perimeter and area of each triangle.

Perimeter: distance around a figure

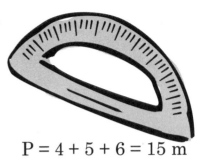

$P = 4 + 5 + 6 = 15$ m

Area: measure of what's inside

$A = 1/2 \ (b \times h)$
$\quad = 1/2 \ (4 \times 5)$
$\quad = 10$ m^2

TIP: *The base and height of a triangle will always be perpendicular.*

1.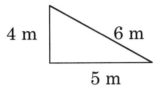

   14 m   14 m   P=
   12 m   A=
   10 m

2.   28 ft.   P=
   40 ft.   52 ft.   A=

3.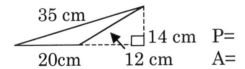

   35 cm
   20cm   12 cm   P=
          14 cm   A=

4.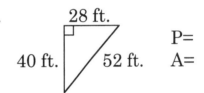

   15 cm
   22 cm   18 cm   P=
           30 cm   A=

5.   40 in   35 in   P=
     30 in   A=
     58 in   A=

6. 12 m   10 m   P=
       8 m   A=
       19 m

7.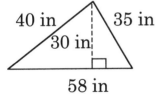

   12 m
   10 m   15 m   P=
                 A=

8.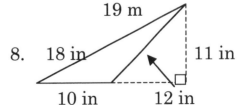

   18 in   11 in
   10 in   12 in   P=
                   A=

Name _____

Measurement: Circumference & Area of Circles

Find the circumference and area of each circle. Use 3.14 for ∏. Round to the nearest hundredth.

Circumference: Distance around 10 in

$$C = \prod \times d$$
$$= 3.14 \times 10$$
$$= 31.4 \text{ in}$$

Area: What's inside 11 m

$$A = \prod \times r^2$$
$$= 3.14 \times 11^2$$
$$= 379.94 \text{ m}^2$$

TIP: *Remember that the diameter is twice the radius.*

1. 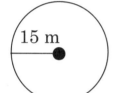 15 m   C=
A=

2. 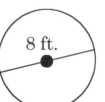 8 ft.   C=
A=

3. 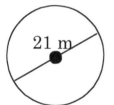 21 m   C=
A=

4. 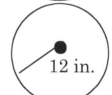 12 in.   C=
A=

5. 2.5 yd.   C=
A=

6. 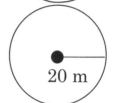 20 m   C=
A=

7. 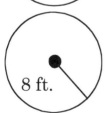 8 ft.   C=
A=

8. 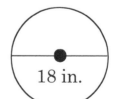 18 in.   C=
A=

 THINK ABOUT IT!

9. Suppose the area of a circle is 31.4 in². About what is the length of the diameter?

76

Integers: Understanding Integers

Name _____

Give the opposite of each idea or integer.

Integers include the set of whole numbers and their opposites. { . . . −3, -2, -1, 0, 1, 2, 3, . . . } $5 profit <u>$5 loss</u>   -10 <u>10</u>

---

1. Increase 12 lbs

   _____

2. 12 mi south

   _____

3. 6 flights up

   _____

4. Saved $25

   _____

5. 8 steps backward

   _____

6. Lose 9 points

   _____

7. Gain 3 lbs

   _____

8. 50 ft below

   _____

9. 92° above zero

   _____

10. 2 steps right

    _____

11. -25

    _____

12. 34

    _____

13. -61

    _____

14. -5

    _____

15. 83

    _____

16. -71

    _____

17. 95

    _____

18. -19

    _____

19. -41

    _____

20. 23

    _____

Integers: Comparing and Ordering

Name _____

Part 1: Compare. Use <, >, or = for each ◯ .

When comparing integers, the integer that is further to the right on the number line has the greater value.

-2 ◯ -3

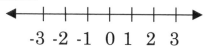

-3 -2 -1 0 1 2 3

-2 is further to the right, so -2 > -3.

1. -4 ◯ 0   2. -6 ◯ -3   3. 0 ◯ -2

4. 1 ◯ -8   5. 4 ◯ -4   6. -3 ◯ -3

7. -11 ◯ -25   8. 6 ◯ 0   9. 5 ◯ -14

10. 1 ◯ -3   11. -7 ◯ -4   12. -3 ◯ -1

Part II: Order from least to greatest

To order from the least to greatest, place them as they would belong on a number line.

13. -2, -6, 1, 0, -8, -4   14. 0, -8, 3, 4, -2

15. 15, -5, 1, -1, 0, 9   16. -2, -7, 0, 11, 7, -14

17. 2, -3, 1, -1, 6, -4   18. 6, -5, -1, 0, 4, -4

 THINK ABOUT IT!

19. The three points marked on the number line represent the integers -40, -60, and -70. Which integer is point X? Y? Z?

    X Y   Z

-75   -50   -25

Integers: Adding Integers

Name _____

Part I: Absolute Value

The **absolute value** of a number is its distance from zero. The following symbol is used when asked to find the absolute value: | |. (Two straight lines surrounding the number.)

| −5 | = 5   −5 is 5 places from zero so its **absolute value** is 5.

Find the absolute value.

1. | −8 | =

2. | 3 | =

3. | 4 | =

4. | −12 | =

5. |−20 | =

6. | 18 | =

7. | −9 | =

8. | −15 | =

9. | 6 | =

10. |−11 | =

Part II: Adding Integers

With the Same Sign
The sum of two positive integers is positive; the sum of two negative integers is negative.

$$-3 + -3 = -6$$
$$4 + 8 = 12$$

With Different Signs
Subtract their absolute values, and use the sign of the greater absolute value.

$$-6 + 8 = 2$$
$$| 8 | - | -6 | =$$
$$\downarrow \qquad \downarrow$$
$$8 \quad - \quad 6 = 2$$

Find each sum.

11. $5 + -3 =$

12. $-2 + -4 =$

13. $8 + -9 =$

14. $-2 + 5 =$

15. $-6 + -1 =$

16. $3 + -1 =$

17. $-9 + 15 =$

18. $0 + -6 =$

19. $-4 + 4 =$

20. $3 + -9 =$

21. $-6 + 4 =$

22. $-6 + -2 =$

Integers: Subtracting Integers

Find each difference.

To subtract integers, add the opposite.

$8 - (-2)$	$-6 - 3$	$-2 - (-4)$
$8 + 2 = 10$	$-6 + -3 = -9$	$-2 + 4 = 2$

TIP: *Don't change the first integer, just the second.*

---

1. $2 - (-3)$

2. $-4 - (-7)$

3. $-5 - (-2)$

4. $-5 - 6$

5. $3 - (-2)$

6. $-6 - 4$

7. $3 - (-5)$

8. $-10 - (-9)$

9. $5 - (-2)$

10. $-7 - (-6)$

11. $7 - (-5)$

12. $-6 - (-8)$

13. $-1 - 5$

14. $-2 - 7$

15. $3 - 8$

16. $4 - (-5)$

17. $7 - (-3)$

18. $7 - 10$

19. $-7 - 0$

20. $-6 - (-6)$

21. $4 - (-1)$

22. $-10 - (-7)$

23. $4 - (-3)$

24. $7 - (-8)$

MATH FACTS

Sir Isaac Newton, is one of the founders of modern mathematics. His formulas help explain gravity — as in, what goes up, must come down. Legend says that Newton was sitting under an apple tree when a falling apple hit his head. This "knock on the head," supposedly lead to some of his math discoveries!

Integers: Multiplying & Dividing

Name _____

Find each product or quotient.

When the signs are the same (both positive or negative) the answer will be positive.

$-8 \times -8 = 64$

$12 \div 2 = 6$

When the signs are different (one positive and one negative) the answer will be negative.

$-9 \div 3 = -3$

$6 \times -8 = -48$

1. 3×-4

2. $-16 \div -4$

3. -5×-5

4. $-20 \div 5$

5. -8×2

6. -4×-2

7. $10 \div -2$

8. 7×-3

9. -3×8

10. $-18 \div 9$

11. $-28 \div -4$

12. 9×3

13. $24 \div -4$

14. 6×-3

15. -5×-3

16. $-35 \div -7$

17. 8×5

18. $-36 \div -9$

19. 4×-8

20. $-49 \div 7$

21. -6×5

22. $18 \div -6$

23. $-30 \div 6$

24. -12×-3

Integers: Problem Solving

Solve each problem.

1. An archaeological dig is located 125 feet above sea level. If the workers dig a hole there that goes 48 feet below sea level, how deep is the hole?

2. At 7:00 a.m. the temperature outside was -5°. At 3:00 p.m., the temperature went up to 21°. How many degrees did the temperature go up from 7 a.m. to 3 p.m.?

3. At 4:00 a.m., the temperature had dropped 13° to a low of -3°. What was the temperature before it dropped?

4. The lowest point in the United States is 282 feet below sea level (Death Valley). The highest point is 20,320 feet above sea level (Mt. McKinley). How much higher is Mt. McKinley than Death Valley?

5. Suppose you were given 13 numbers and asked to find their product. Seven of the numbers were positive, and the rest were negative. Would your product be positive or negative?

6. If **a** represents a negative integer and **b** represents a positive integer, will their product be positive or negative?

7. Suppose that **a** represents a negative integer and **b** represents a positive integer.
   a. When will a^b be positive?
   b. When will a^b be negative?

1.	
2.	
3.	
4.	
5.	
6.	
7.	

Algebra: Evaluating Algebraic Expressions   Name _____

Evaluate each algebraic expression.

$n + 12$ for $n = 10$ 1. Replace the variable with the number.
$10 + 12 = 22$ 2. Do the computation.

TIP: *Remember to work inside parentheses first.*

1. $25 - x$ for $x = 15$ 2. $a \div 5$ for $a = 35$

3. $x + 36$ for $x = 20$ 4. $r + 26$ for $r = 9$

5. $b - 15$ for $b = 40$ 6. $x \div 9$ for $x = 36$

7. $a \times 4$ for $a = 6$ 8. $17 - a$ for $a = 17$

9. $(x + y) - 4$ for $x = 10$ and $y = 6$ 10. $(5 \times a) + 7$ for $a = 4$

11. $(a - 2) \times b$ for $a = 8$ and $b = 6$ 12. $2 + x + 10$ for $x = 9$

13. $(3 \times c) + 4$ for $c = 5$ 14. $20 - (a \div 2)$ for $a = 6$

15. $7 \times (6 - x)$ for $x = 3$ 16. $(2 \times a) + b$ for $a = 5$ and $b = 6$

Evaluate each algebraic expression for $x = 2$, $y = 4$ and $z = 7$.

17. $(x + y) + 10$ 18. $y + (z - x)$

19. $y \div x + z$ 20. $8 \times (z - y)$

21. $x + (y - 3)$ 22. $z - x$

23. $z - y + 9$ 24. $x + y + z$

Algebra: Solving Equations With Addition & Subtraction

Solve and check each equation.

$x - 17 = 28$
$x - 17 \underline{+ 17} = 28 \underline{+ 17}$
$x = 45$
Check: $45 - 17 = 28$

1. Look at what has been done to the variable.
2. Undo it using the inverse (opposite) operation on both sides of the equation.

---

1. $n + 37 = 83$

2. $n + 66 = 82$

3. $x + 37 = 95$

4. $x + 49 = 72$

5. $c - 56 = 12$

6. $x + 17 = 38$

7. $c - 8.9 = 1.7$

8. $c + 28 = 49$

9. $x - 77 = 43$

10. $y - 79 = 24$

11. $c - 48 = 15$

12. $n - 55 = 32$

13. $x - 26 = 95$

14. $n - 18 = 97$

15. $c - 2.7 = 3.8$

16. $x - 86 = 58$

17. $34 = x + 7$

18. $1.4 = y - 6.5$

19. $3.5 = a + 1.9$

20. $28 = n - 14$

21. $x + 27 = 46$

22. $18 = y - 25$

23. $n - 57 = 39$

24. $6.4 = c + 2.8$

$\sqrt{49} = 7$

Algebra: Solving Equations With Multiplication & Division

Solve and check each equation.

$8n = 520$
$8n \div 8 = 520 \div 8$
$n = 65$
Check: $8 \times 65 = 520$

1. Look at what has been done to the variable.
2. Undo it using the inverse (opposite) operation on both sides of the equation.

---

1. $4x = 68$

2. $9y = 99$

3. $2c = 88$

4. $6x = 48$

5. $12n = 144$

6. $9x = 234$

7. $21n = 168$

8. $5y = 115$

9. $43y = 172$

10. $54x = 162$

11. $72y = 432$

12. $32a = 192$

13. $b \div 41 = 5$

14. $c \div 26 = 5$

15. $y \div 32 = 9$

16. $x \div 24 = 8$

17. $y \div 32 = 16$

18. $x \div 44 = 15$

19. $b \div 23 = 11$

20. $x \div 16 = 12$

21. $94 = c \div 5$

22. $n \div 38 = 67$

23. $x \div 75 = 28$

24. $n \div 87 = 38$

25. $18c = 216$

26. $192 \div x = 12$

Algebra: Problem Solving

Name _____

Solve each problem.

1. After depositing $15 into her account, Stacey had $203 in the account. How much money was in the account before this deposit?

1. _____

2. Ray ran 12 miles in 3 days. If he ran 4.2 miles the first day and 3.4 miles the second day, how many miles did he run the third day?

2. _____

3. Ricardo bought 8 boxes of markers. There was the same number in each box. He bought 72 markers. How many were in each box?

3. _____

4. Billy ate 3 times more hot dogs than Charlie in the food eating contest at Miller Grove Middle School. Billy ate 15 hot dogs. How many did Charlie eat?

4. _____

5. The length of a rectangular flower bed is 3 times the width. The length is 42 ft. What is the width?

5. _____

6. Tammy sold 360 tickets for the fundraiser this year, which was 4 times as many as she sold last year. How many tickets did she sell last year?

6. _____

7. Gardner Tire Service sold 124 of the same kind of tires in one week and made $18,600 on those sales. How much does each tire cost?

7. _____

Probability & Statistics: Chances & Probability

Determine the probability of each situation. Express each answer as a fraction in lowest terms.

Flip a coin. What is the probability it will land on heads? Tails?

P(H) = 1/2

P(T) = 1/2

Since there are 2 sides, one head and one tails, there is a 1 out of 2 (1/2) chance it will land on either side.

Roll a die.

1. odd number   1._____
2. even number   2._____
3. a number less than 3   3._____
4. a number greater than 2   4._____
5. 3   5._____
6. a number less than 7   6._____

Pick a card (or cards) from a standard deck of fifty-two cards.

7. a jack of spades   7._____
8. a four of hearts   8._____
9. a black eleven   9._____
10. a six   10._____
11. a red card   11._____
12. a queen or a king   12._____
13. a diamond   13._____
14. a red ace   14._____

 THINK ABOUT IT!

15. Suppose you have a basket of 100 leaves. You know that P(green) = 3/5 and P(brown) = 2/5.

   What can you say about the basket of leaves?

Probability & Statistics: Making Tree Diagrams

Draw a tree diagram to illustrate each probability.

A tree diagram is used to show the total number of possible outcomes in a probability experiment.

flip a coin 2 times

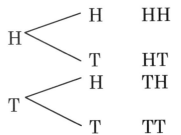

1. choosing chocolate or vanilla ice cream and chocolate or vanilla cake

2. choosing a red or black blouse and a black or white skirt

3. choosing raisin bran or frosted flakes and skim or whole milk

LG

4. rolling a die and flipping a coin

5. choosing toast, a bagel, or a biscuit and jelly, butter, or cream cheese

6. choosing a comedy, horror, or drama movie and popcorn or candy

Probability & Statistics: Reading Graphs Name _____

Use the following bar graph to answer the questions below.

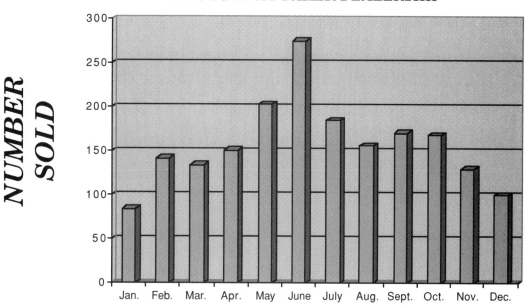

CARS SOLD AT BAKER DEALERSHIP

1. What is the title of the graph?

2. What is on the horizontal axis?

3. How is the vertical axis labeled?

4. In which month was the greatest number of cars sold?

5. In which month was the least number of cars sold?

6. Which two consecutive months show the greatest change in car sales?

7. Approximately how many cars were sold in September?

8. Based on the graph, in which season should the dealership try to do more advertising? Explain.

Probability & Statistics: Mean, Median and Mode

Find the mean, median, and mode of each set of data. Round to the nearest tenth.

> **6, 7, 7, 8, 7, 5**
>
> *Mean* (or average): Add the numbers and divide by the total number in set.
> $(6 + 7 + 7 + 8 + 7 + 5) \div 6 = 40 \div 6 = 6.7$ Mean = 6.7
>
> *Median* (middle number): Place the numbers in order. Find the middle number. If there is not one middle number, average the two in the middle. 5, 6, 7, 7, 7, 8 The two middle numbers are 7. $(7 + 7) \div 2 = 7$. Median = 7
>
> *Mode* (most frequent): Find the number that occurs most frequently.
> Mode = 7

1. 2, 8, 6, 4, 3, 2, 4

2. 8, 13, 14, 12, 9, 14, 10

3. 23, 22, 28, 26, 18, 20, 25, 23

4. 50, 45, 16, 20, 35, 24

5. 45, 45, 70, 40, 60, 42, 42, 60, 42

6. 71, 62, 58, 34, 43, 56, 12

7. 16, 10, 9, 4, 3, 15, 24, 8, 8, 12

8. 143, 150, 132, 145, 125, 100

9. 150, 250, 125, 200, 100, 175, 275

10. 200, 100, 350, 600, 150, 400, 350

Solve each problem.

1. David's company is giving away 5 free trips to Hawaii to the employees. There are 125 employees in his company. What is the probability that David will win a trip to Hawaii?

2. Decide whether this game is fair: Roll a number cube with the numbers 1-6. If it lands on an odd number, you win. If not, your opponent wins.

3. One postcard will be drawn out of 1,000 received for free concert tickets. You mailed in 30 postcards. What are your chances of winning the tickets?

4. George and his twin sister are among 3 boys and 5 girls nominated for an honors band. One boy and one girl will be selected at random. What are each of their chances of being selected?

5. Fifty-four teenagers were given a choice of "more CD's" or "more clothes" for a birthday gift. Twice as many picked "more CD's" than "more clothes." How many picked each?

6. The mean of five numbers is 18. Four of the numbers are 13, 17, 26, and 18. What is the fifth number?

7. The mean of four numbers if 175. Three of the numbers are 162, 230, and 178. What is the fourth number?

1.

2.

3.

4.

5.

6.

7.

ANSWER KEY

Page 5 1. B, 2. C, 3. B, 4. D, 5. B, 6. D, 7. C, 8. B, 9. A, 10. B, 11. A, 12. C, 13. C, 14. D, 15. C, 16. B

Page 6 17. A, 18. C, 19. C, 20. A, 21. C, 22. C, 23. D, 24. A, 25. A, 26. D, 27. A

Page 7 28. C, 29. C, 30. B, 31. C, 32. A, 33. A, 34. C, 35. B, 36. B, 37. C

Page 8 38. B, 39. B, 40. C, 41. D, 42. A, 43. B, 44. D, 45. D, 46. A, 47. B, 48. C, 49. C, 50. A

Page 9 1. 8 tens, 2. 9 hundred, 3. 8 ones, 4. 30 thousand, 5. 5 thousand, 6. 600 thousand, 7. 4 million, 8. 10 million, 9. 100 million, 10. 400 million, 11. 20 million, 12. 1 million, 13. 7 billion, 14. 300 billion, 15. 80 billion 16. (Answers will vary.) Sample: 365,421,677; 364,421,677.

Page 10 1. 7,260, 2. 63,437, 3. 33,303, 4. 49,449 5. 71,097, 6. 80,014, 7. 52,006, 8. 45,045, 9. 375,175, 10. 123,881, 11. 554,601, 12. 202,154, 13. 6,600,321, 14. 80,250,302, 15. 230,509,003.

Page 11 1. 90, 2. 500, 3. 700, 4. 290, 5. 3,600, 6. 5,000, 7. 6,000, 8. 37,000, 9. 70,000, 10. 62,000, 11. 60,000, 12. 24,900, 13. 70,000, 14. 52,000, 15. 600,000, 16. 300,000, 17. 683,000, 18. 30,000, 19. 189,100, 20. 700,000, 21. No, you need precise digits; yes, the age does not have to be exact.

Page 12 1. 50, 2. 60, 3. 50, 4. 70, 5. 50, 6. 70, 7. 400, 8. 700, 9. 800, 10. 100, 11. 400, 12. 1,400, 13. 7,000, 14. 5,000, 15. 2,000, 16. 7,000, 17. 2,000, 18. 10,000, 19. 6,000, 20. 1,000, 21. $3,000.

Page 13

	A	B	C	D	E
1.	37	28	63	44	72
2.	59	69	287	380	702
3.	853	819	1,120	2,025	3,940
4.	7,937	7,796	50,839	52,146	141,945
5.	73	137	392	941	– – – –
6.	761	2,138	9,891	238	– – – –

Page 14 1. 42, 2. 31, 3. 50, 4. 79, 5. 68, 6. 13, 7. 35, 8. 54, 9. 10, 10. 19, 11. 211, 12. 646, 13. 313, 14. 98, 15. 185, 16. 5,101, 17. 4,045, 18. 3,656, 19. 1,610, 20. 990, 21. 50,920, 22. 65,993, 23. 3,199, 24. 26,055, 25. 50,795, 26. 53, 27. 58, 28. 563, 29. 108, 30. 4,908

Page 15 1. 344, 2. 450, 3. 174, 4. 1,358, 5. 1,970, 6. 9,588, 7. 35,028, 8. 218,432, 9. 2,820, 10. 25,120, 11. 87,740, 12. 156,800, 13.1,196, 14. 7,030, 15. 171,080, 16. 363,426, 17. 408, 18. 5,535, 19. 35,960, 20. 177,463, 21. Subtract 287 from 11,480.

Page 16 1. 28 R 2, 2. 14, 3. 14 R 1, 4. 23 R 3, 5. 33 R 1, 6. 82 R 3, 7. 96 R 4, 8. 396, 9. 4 R 12, 10. 70 R 16, 11. 3 R 26, 12. 6 R 4, 13. 1,044, 14. 951 R 5, 15. 1,398 R 1, 16. 413 R 2

Page 17 1. 13, 2. 18, 3. 18, 4. 2, 5. 9, 6. 6, 7. 21, 8. 3, 9. 5, 10. 11, 11. 8, 12. 19, 13. 35, 14. 14, 15. 18, 16. 7, 17. 3, 18. 2, 19. 20, 20. 27, 21. 36

Page 18 1. 14, 2. 36, 3. 10, 4. $3, 5. 107, 6. $90, 7. 38 8. 661

Page 19 1. 8 thousandths, 2. 2 hundredths, 3. 8 tenths, 4. 2 ten-thousandths, 5. 7 thousandths, 6. 7 hundredths, 7. 9 tenths, 8. 8 thousandths, 9. 9 ten-thousandths, 10. 3 hundredths, 11. 3 thousandths, 12. 3 tenths, 13. 6 hundredths, 14. 6 ten-thousandths, 15. 7 ten-thousandths, 16. 7 hundredths, 17. 5 thousandths, 18. 2 thousandths, 19. 8 tenths, 20. 2 ten-thousandths, 21. 2 hundredths, 22. 0.0384; 47.65

Page 20 1. 6.5, 2. 11.4, 3. 7.2, 4. 14.1, 5. 31.9, 6. 9.18, 7. 16.37, 8. 43.08, 9. 81.22, 10. 200.31, 11. 49.49, 12. 10.27, 13. 305.1, 14. 28.212, 15. 18.961, 16. 500.002

Page 21 1. 141.37, 2. 40, 3. 15.3, 4. 4.297, 5. .1, 6. 27.79, 7. 546.08, 8. 3.2, 9. 13.08, 10. 444, 11. 4.1, 12. 607.8, 13. 16.654, 14. 67.3, 15. 6, 16. 2.76, 17. 5.5, 18. 6.29, 19. 21, 20. 99.4, 21. 635.682, 22. 59.6, 23. 18, 24. 53.6, 25. 27 days

Page 22 1. >, 2. >, 3. >, 4. =, 5. <, 6. <, 7. <, 8. <, 9. >, 10. =, 11. <, 12. <, 13. 6.45, 6.457, 6.46, 6.461; 14. .06, .6, .606, 6.6; 15. 14.012, 14.120, 14.201, 14.210; 16. .912, 1.92, 9.12, 19.2; 17. .035, .35, 3.05, 3.50; 18. .0458, .4058, .4508, .458

Page 23 1. 21, 2. 14, 3. 16, 4. 1, 5. 105, 6. 90, 7. 16, 8. 6, 9. 0, 10. 9, 11. 90, 12. 9, 13. 40, 14. 45, 15. 160, 16. 28, 17. 80, 18. 120, 19. 1, 20. 26, 21. 48, 22. 98, 23. 40, 24. 280, 25. 67, 26. 12, 27. 3, 28. 80

Page 24 1. .98, 2. 76.63, 3. 242.86, 4. 714.24, 5. 38.2167, 6. 43.45, 7. 3.432, 8. 53.38, 9. .92, 10. 46.48, 11. .172, 12. 8.594, 13. 291.5, 14. 89.94, 15. 101.6, 16. 82.45, 17. .576, 18. 4.226, 19. 566.9, 20. 2.16, 21. 47.05, 22. 1.243, 23. 11.43, 24. .874, 25. no

Page 25 1. 13.5, 2. .3828, 3. .5, 4. 11.952, 5. 208.26, 6. .152, 7. 456.659, 8. 4.48, 9. 9.243, 10. 4.724, 11. 63.95, 12. .181, 13. 121.33, 14. 26.67, 15. 18.3, 16. 63.828, 17. 15.93, 18. 151.712, 19. false; .9 + .9 = 1.8 (Examples may vary.)

Page 26 1. yes, by 0.006 cm, 2. $24.27, 3. $13.50, 4. $15.90, 5. a. 2.52, b. 3.78, c. 2.1, d. .42, e. 1.68, f. .51, g. 1.21, h. .79, i. .23, j. 1.07, k. 2.37

Page 27 1. 40, 2. 28, 3. 63, 4. 260, 5. 680, 6. 12, 7. 30, 8. 32, 9. 42, 10. 36, 11. 300, 12. 140, 13. 2,800, 14. 30,000, 15. 600, 16. 100, 17. 120, 18. 250, 19. 400, 20. 400, 21. 125, 22. A

Page 28

	$\times 10$	$\times 100$	$\times 1000$
1.	168.792	1,687.92	16,879.2
2.	89.034	890.34	8903.4
3.	220.0154	2,200.154	22,001.54
4.	368.35	3,683.5	36,835
5.	586.78	5,867.8	58,678
6.	710.803	7,108.03	71,080.3
7.	2,804.51	28,045.1	280,451
8.	3,768.9	37,689	376,890
9.	1,010.12	10,101.2	101,012
10.	350.5	3,505	35,050
11.	785.9	7,859	78,590
12.	6,032	60,320	603,200
13.	486.7	4,867	48,670
14.	930.1	9,301	93,010

Page 29 1. 1.2, 2. .24, 3. 2.538, 4. .685, 5. 30.08, 6. .0615, 7. 2.275, 8. 56.96, 9. 4.6284, 10. 11.297, 11. .39042, 12. 56.342, 13. 21.76, 14. 5.376, 15. 1.4952, 16. .4464, 17. 5.085, 18. 796.136, 19. 85.33, 20. 9.28

Page 30 1. .018, 2. .0024, 3. .065, 4. .0315, 5. .0172, 6. .0336, 7. .0003, 8. .0143, 9. .00648, 10. 5.38, 11. .00049, 12. 3.604, 13. .0012, 14. .0135, 15. 1.9992, 16. 19.4688, 17. 1.77735, 18. .43125, 19. 34.4258, 20. .8164

Page 31 1. 90, 2. 90, 3. 80, 4. 70, 5. 40, 6. 60, 7. 5, 8. 6, 9. 50, 10. 8, 11. 9, 12. 40, 13. 50, 14. 10, 15. 10

Page 32

	$\div 10$	$\div 100$	$\div 1000$
1.	278.9317	27.89137	2.789137
2.	343.0052	34.30052	3.430052
3.	160.583	16.0583	1.60583
4.	725.994	72.5994	7.25994
5.	68.13	6.813	.6813
6.	54.59	5.459	.5459
7.	45.32	4.532	.4532
8.	98.603	9.8603	.98603
9.	21.07	2.107	.2107
10.	.6253	.06253	.006253
11.	.7102	.07102	.007102
12.	1.3	.13	.013
13.	20.6	2.06	.206

Page 33 1. 16.8, 2. 8.93, 3. 6.48, 4. .574, 5. 3.78, 6. 3.55, 7. 5.981, 8. 4.381, 9. 5.67, 10. 4.35, 11. 18.96, 12. 6.84, 13. .873, 14. .033, 15. 72.5, 16. .076

Page 34 1. 7, 2. .48, 3. 3.8, 4. 64.1, 5. 6.4, 6. 5.2, 7. 7.3, 8. 2.3, 9. 16.3, 10. 2.1, 11. 7.3, 12. 16, 13. 62, 14. 58, 15. 450, 16. 7.52

Page 35 1. 1.4×10^5, 2. 6.49×10^7, 3. 4×10^{-4}, 4. 9.9×10^7, 5. 3.5×10^5, 6. 1.5×10^{-5}, 7. 3.8×10^{-4}, 8. 7.2×10^6, 9. 1.3×10^{10}, 10. 5.4×10^{-5}, 11. 9×10^{-5}, 12. 2.5×10^6, 13. 10,300,000, 14. .000000047, 15. .37, 16. 52,000,000,000,000, 17. 469.8, 18. .0000512, 19. 2,100,000, 20. .00068, 21. 760,000

Page 36 1. $5.34, 2. $27, 3. .06 in, 4. $2.65, 5. $2.02, 6. $.02, 7. $1.17, 8. $14.16, 9. $635.25

Page 37 1. $6 \cdot 6$, 2. $8 \cdot 8 \cdot 8 \cdot 8$, 3. $2 \cdot 2 \cdot 2 \cdot 2 \cdot 2$, 4. $10 \cdot 10 \cdot 10$, 5. $7 \cdot 7 \cdot 7 \cdot 7 \cdot 7$, 6. $9 \cdot 9 \cdot 9 \cdot 9 \cdot 9 \cdot 9$, 7. $3 \cdot 3$, 8. $4 \cdot 4 \cdot 4$, 9. $5 \cdot 5 \cdot 5 \cdot 5$, 10. 3^3, 11. 12^2, 12. 6^4, 13. 5^2, 14. 7^5, 15. 8^3, 16. 2^4, 17. 9^3, 18. 10^4, 19. 121, 20. 125, 21. 2401, 22. 27, 23. 100, 24. 59049

Page 38 1. C, 2. C, 3. P, 4. C, 5. P, 6. C, 7. P, 8. C, 9. P, 10. C, 11. C, 12. P, 13. C, 14. C, 15. C, 16. P, 17. C, 18. C, 19. C, 20. C, 21. C, 22. C, 23. P, 24. C, 25. P, 26. P, 27. C, 28. P, 29. (Answers will vary.) 3, 5; 5, 7; 17, 19

Page 39

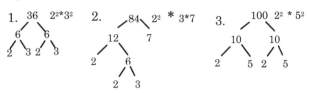

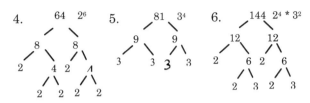

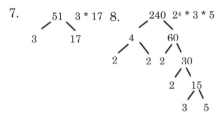

7. 51 3 * 17   8. 240 2⁴ * 3 * 5

Page 40   1. 3, 2. 8, 3. 4, 4. 4, 5. 3, 6. 8, 7. 4, 8. 9, 9. 15, 10. 7, 11. 9, 12. 26, 13. 14, 14. 4, 15. 18

Page 41   1. 4, 2. 6, 3. 24, 4. 18, 5. 20, 6. 12, 7. 15, 8. 10, 9. 60, 10. 40, 11. 12, 12. 30, 13. 16, 14. 36, 15. 60

Page 42   1. 12 in, 2. 5, 180, 3. yes, at 36 feet, 4. rabbit; 8 more jumps, 5. 9, 6. 1 x 36; 2 x 18; 4 x 9; 6 x 6

Page 43   1. 6, 2. 4, 3. 3, 4. 10, 5. 14, 6. 15, 7. 12, 8. 32, 9. 28, 10. 16, 11. 50, 12. 15, 13. 15, 14. 45, 15. 30, 16. 50, 17. 30, 18. 36, 19. 24, 20. 42, 21. 4, 22. 24, 23. 16, 24. 36, 25. Mon. & Wed.

Page 44   1. 3/4, 2. 1/5, 3. 1/5, 4. 1/2, 5. 7/8, 6. 5/6, 7. 1/2, 8. 1/3, 9. 3/4, 10. 3/8, 11. 8/15, 12. 2/3, 13. 1/2, 14. 9/10, 15. 2/15, 16. 1/3, 17. 1/4, 18. 3/4, 19. 4/5, 20. 3/4, 21. 1/2, 22. 4/9, 23. 1/3, 24. 3/4, 25. 1, 3, 5, 7, 11, 13, 17

Page 45   1. =, 2. <, 3. >, 4. <, 5. >, 6. >, 7. >, 8. <, 9. >, 10. >, 11. >, 12. =, 13. =, 14. <, 15. <, 16. 3/8, 3/7, 3/4, 17. 1/5, 1/4, 1/3, 18. 1/4, 2/5, 1/2, 3/5, 19. 2/3, 13/18, 7/9, 5/6, 20. 2/9, 2/7, 2/5, 2/3, 21. 1/2, 2/3, 3/4, 4/5

Page 46   1. 3 2/5, 2. 3 1/2, 3. 6 1/2, 4. 4, 5. 4 1/2, 6. 2 1/5, 7. 3 1/3, 8. 6, 9. 4 1/2, 10. 2 1/3, 11. 5 1/4, 12. 1 1/5, 13. 6 1/3, 14. 1 1/3, 15. 5 1/2, 16. 11/3, 17. 25/4, 18. 17/8, 19. 29/5, 20. 19/10, 21. 35/8, 22. 37/5, 23. 65/7, 24. 43/5, 25. 46/7, 26. 17/7, 27. 46/9, 28. 9/2, 29. 31/8, 30. 31/4

Page 47   1. .75, 2. .4, 3. .25. 4. .17, 5. .88, 6. .43, 7. .8, 8. .33, 9. .2, 10. .6, 11. .67, 12. .83, 13. .38, 14. .9, 15. .22, 16. .63, 17. .31, 18. 3.5, 19. .44, 20. .13, 21. .35, 22. 2.83, 23. 1.83, 24. .77, 25. .17, 26. 1.6, 27. .56, 28. .47, 29. .56, 30. .48, 31. .28, 32. .7

Page 48   1. 5/11, 2. 4/5, 3. 3/4, 4. 1, 5. 0, 6. 1/2, 7. 1 3/8, 8. 1/2, 9. 3/10, 10. 1, 11. 7 5/8, 12. 5 1/3, 13. 10 2/3, 14. 7, 15. 35 1/4, 16. 3 1/2

Page 49   1. 5/8, 2. 1 1/12, 3. 1/21, 4. 1 11/20, 5. 2/5, 6. 1 1/15, 7. 1 1/4, 8. 1 1/6, 9. 1 5/8, 10. 7/12, 11. 1 5/24, 12. 7/10, 13. 5/18, 14. 13/20, 15.1 21/40 16. 1/18, 17. a. more, b. more, c. less

Page 50   1. 15 1/6, 2. 8 7/12, 3. 7 1/4, 4. 8 5/8, 5. 6 3/8, 6. 8 3/4, 7. 12 1/3, 8. 3 1/10, 9. 10 5/12, 10. 5/12, 11. 11 5/6, 12. 1 1/6, 13. 17 7/8, 14. 4 3/10, 15. 33 3/20, 16. 11 1/6, 17. 4 7/10, 18. 6 1/2

Page 51   1. 4 pages, 2. 1/2 mile, 3. Billy; 3/10 mile, 4. 3 3/4 inches, 5. 1 3/4 hour, 6. 15 15/16 inches, 7. no; combining the flour is 6 1/4 cup

Page 52   1. 1/8, 2. 10 1/2, 3. 1/15, 4. 15, 5. 2/5, 6. 10 9/20, 7. 3 1/3, 8. 14 1/2, 9. 3/10, 10. 7 7/8, 11. 5/8, 12. 3, 13. 1/6, 14. 19 1/6, 15. 3 1/3, 16. 9 1/3, 17. 3 1/2, 18. 46 1/2, 19. 3/14, 20. 26 5/6, 21. less than one; 6/5 •5/6 = 1 (Examples may vary.)

Page 53   1. 7 1/2, 2. 2 2/5, 3. 20, 4. 1 7/8, 5. 10 2/3, 6. 2/21, 7. 8/9, 8. 1 1/2, 9. 2, 10. 2 1/10, 11. 1/2, 12. 33/104, 13. 1 1/6, 14. 1 3/4, 15. 1 1/3, 16. 8, 17. 10, 18. 2 1/11

Page 54   1. 45, 2. 5, 3. 5 1/4 ft, 4. 15 minutes, 5. about 23, 6. 2 3/4 days, 7. 18 hours

Page 55   1. 5/6, 5:6, 5 to 6; 2. 30/40, 30:40, 30 to 40; 3. 2/3, 2:3, 2 to 3; 4. 7/8, 7:8, 7 to 8; 5. 6/11, 6:11, 6 to 11; 6. 23/41, 23:41, 23 to 41; 7. 2/5, 2:5, 2 to 5; 8. 9/10, 9:10, 9 to 10; 9. 12/25, 12:25, 12 to 25; 10. 13/25, 13:25, 13 to 25; 11. 1/28, 1:28, 1 to 28; 12. 3/45, 3:45, 3 to 45; 13. 3/5, 3:5, 3 to 5; 14. 12/4, 12:4, 12 to 4; 15. 2/3, 2:3, 2 to 3; 16. 9/4, 9:4, 9 to 4; 17. boys

Page 56   1. yes, 2. no, 3. no, 4. yes, 5. yes, 6. yes, 7. no, 8. yes, 9. no, 10. no, 11. yes, 12. yes, 13. yes, 14. yes, 15. no, 16. yes, 17. no, 18. yes, 19. no, 20. no, 21. yes, 22. yes, 23. no, 24. yes

Page 57   1. 48, 2. 75, 3. 10, 4. 14, `5. 20, 6. 60, 7. 18, 8. 21, 9. 8, 10. 80, 11. 36, 12. 6, 13. 8, 14. 75, 15. 21, 16. 70, 17. 84, 18. 40, 19. 55, 20. 20, 21. 60, 22. 63, 23. 49, 24. 6, 25. a. less, b. more, c. less

age 58 1. 2/3 = n/24; 16, 2. 12/100 = n/150; 18, 3. 3/96 = n/72; 27, 4. 6/14 = n/588; 252, 5. 3/4 = n/28; 21 ogs, 6. 4/8 = n/12; 6 pounds, 7. 7/2 = n/5; 17.5 mi

age 59 1. 19%, 2. 41%, 3. 13%, 4. 29%, 5. 57%, 6. 1%, 7. 17%, 8. 83%, 9. 64%, 10. 73%, 11. 51%, 12. 5%, 13. 1/50, 14. 11/25, 15. 9/50, 16. 1/2, 17. 91/100, 3. 73/100, 19. 21/25, 20. 1/5, 21. 13/20, 22. 33/100, 23. 4, 24. 1/10, 25. 19/20, 26. 9/20, 27. 7/10, 28. 43/50, 9. (Responses may vary.) The player put in a upendous performance and gave it his all.

age 60 1. 9%, 2. 21%, 3. 38%, 4. 79%, 5. 65%, 6. 5%, 7. 44%, 8. 3%, 9. 99%, 10. 87%, 11. 61%, 12. 33%, 3. 82%, 14. 53%, 15. 6%, 16. 20%, 17. 1%, 18. 47%, 9. 58%, 20. 34%, 21. 25%, 22. 73%, 23. 60%, 24. 15%, 5. 27%, 26. 84%, 27. 93%, 28. 41%

age 61 1. 75%, 2. 20%, 3. 38%, 4. 40%, 5. 60%, 6. 5%, 7. 58%, 8. 73%, 9. 50%, 10. 70%, 11. 85%, 12. 7%, 13. 64%, 14. 71%, 15. 76%, 16. 63%, 17. 36%, 18. 5%, 19. 60%, 20. 38%, 21. 95%, 22. 83%, 23. 80%, 24. 3%, 25. 62%, 26. 76%, 27. 53%, 28. 98%

age 62 1. .51, 2. .28, 3. .09, 4. .3, 5. .16, 6. .73, 7. 54, 8. .82, 9. .55, 10. .96, 11. 2.1, 12. .48, 13. 1/2, 4. 1/4, 15. 3/100, 16. 4/5, 17. 19/20, 18. 61/100, 19. 1/50, 20. 33/100, 21. 73/100, 22. 19/50, 23. 21/25, 24. 7/100, 25. 27%, .45, 1/2, .6, 74/100, 90%

age 63 1. 24, 2. 3.5, 3. 8, 4. 60.16, 5. 32, 6. 10.8 , 4.5, 8. 7.2, 9. 2.2, 10. .96, 11. 8.64, 12. 72.2, 13. 6.55, 14. 4.94, 15. 20.88, 16. 16, 17. 13, 18. 72, 19. 25, 0. 49, 21. 214.4, 22. a. 10.92, b. 10.92, c. 109.2

age 64 1. 8, 2. 19%; 81%, 3. 39%, 4. 63%, 5. $1,550, . $150; $100

age 65 1. straight, 2. obtuse, 3. right, 4. obtuse 5. cute, 6. straight, 7. right, 8. acute, 9. obtuse, 10. cute, 11. right, 12. straight, 13. same size; no

age 66 Key: **S** = Square; **R** = Rectangle; **Rh** = hombus; **P** = Parallelogram; **T** = Trapezoid; . S, R, Rh, P, 2. T, 3. P, 4. R, P, 5. S, R, Rh, P, 6. S, R, h, P, 7. T, 8. R, P, 9. Rh, P, 10. P, 11. S, R, Rh, P, 12.

age 67 1. isosceles, obtuse, 2. scalene, right, 3. calene, obtuse, 4. equilateral, acute, 5. isosceles, ight, 6. isosceles, acute, 7. scalene, obtuse, 8. scalene, ight, 9. equilateral, acute, 10. isosceles, acute

Page 68 1. 2. 3. 4. None
5. Infinite 6. 7. None 8. 9.
10. 11. 12. None

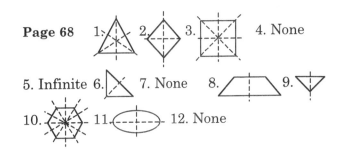

Page 69 1. similar, 2. congruent, 3. neither, 4. congruent, 5. neither, 6. similar,

Page 70 1. 33, 2. 2 1/4, 3. 4 1/2, 4. 10000, 5. 40, 6. 10560, 7. 5, 8. 24, 9. 15, 10. 180, 11. 3, 12. 16, 13. 3, 14. 2, 15. 120, 16. 8, 17. 3, 18. 8, 19. 5000, 20. 64, 21. 3, 22. 36, 23. 432, 24. 32

Page 71 1. 4 lb 8 oz, 2. 13 ft 11 in, 3. 1 ft 5 in, 4. 6 lb 4 oz, 5. 2 lb 10 oz 6. 9 lb 15 oz, 7. 1 ft 4 in, 8. 10 ft 3 in, 9. 13 ft 6 in, 10. 6 lb 2 oz, 11. 16 ft, 12. 3 ft 11 in, 13. 25 ft 6 in, 14. 3 lb 7 oz, 15. 4 lb 2 oz, 16. 1 ft 7 in, 17. 9 ft 3 in, 18. 40 ft 10 in

Page 72 1. 354, 2. .542, 3. 4332, 4. 947, 5. .39, 6. 4850, 7. .046, 8. 75, 9. 2.56, 10. 704, 11. 6.367, 12. 1330, 13. 19000, 14. 6500, 15. 320, 16. 1.264, 17. .736, 18. .00185, 19. 220000, 20. .012, 21. .0014, 22. .007, 23. .22, 24. 500

Page 73 1. 66 yd 2 ft, 2. 3 lbs, 3. 8 1/4 in, 4. 860000 mg, 5. 4.565 L, 6. 435 kg; 435000000 mg
7. 800 oz, 8. 6000 mL

Page 74 1. P = 20 m, A = 25 m², 2. P = 28 m, A = 40 m², 3. P = 84 cm, A = 300 cm², 4. P = 24 cm, A = 36 cm², 5. P = 76 m, A = 320 m², 6. P = 48 yd, A = 80 yd², 7. P = 36 ft, A = 81 ft², 8. P = 110 ft, A = 400 ft², 9. Area will double; area will triple. (Examples will vary.)

Page 75 1. P = 38 m, A = 60 m², 2. P = 120 ft, A = 560 ft², 3. P = 67 cm, A = 140 cm², 4. P = 70 cm, A = 135 cm², 5. P = 133 in, A = 870 in², 6. P = 41 m, A = 76 m², 7. P = 37 m, A = 60 m², 8. P = 40 in, A = 55 in²

Page 76 1. C = 94.2 m, A = 706.5 m², 2. C = 25.12 ft, A = 50.24 ft², 3. C = 65.94 m, A = 346.19 m², 4. C = 75.36 in, A = 452.16 in², 5. C = 7.85 yd, A = 4.91 yd², 6. C= 125.6 m, A = 1256 m², 7. C = 50.24 ft, A = 200.96 ft², 8. C = 56.52 in, A = 254.34 in², 9. about 6

Page 77 1. decrease 12 lbs, 2. 12 mi north, 3. 6 flights down, 4. spent $25, 5. 8 steps forward, 6. gain 9 points, 7. lose 3 lbs, 8. 50 ft above, 9. 92° below zero, 10. 2 steps left, 11. 25, 12. −34, 13. 61, 14. 5, 15. −83, 16. 71, 17. −95, 18. 19, 19. 41, 20. −23

Page 78 1. <, 2. <, 3. >, 4. >, 5. >, 6. =, 7. >, 8. >, 9. >, 10. >, 11. <, 12. <, 13. -8, -6, -4, -2, 0, 1, 14. -8, -2, 0, 3, 4, 15. -5, -1, 0, 9, 15, 16. -14, -7, -2, 0, 7, 11, 17. -4, -3, -1, 1, 2, 6, 18. -5, -4, -1, 0, 4, 6, 19. X = -70, Y = -60, Z = -40

Page 79 1. 8, 2. 3, 3. 4, 4. 12, 5. 20, 6. 18, 7. 9, 8. 15, 9. 6, 10. 11, 11. 2, 12. −6, 13. −1, 14. 3, 15. −7, 16. 2, 17. 6, 18. −6, 19. 0, 20. −6, 21. −2, 22. −8

Page 80 1. 5, 2. 3, 3. −3, 4. −11, 5. 5, 6. −10, 7. 8, 8. −1, 9. 7, 10. −1, 11. 12, 12. 2, 13. −6, 14. −9, 15. −5, 16. 9, 17. 10, 18. −3, 19. −7, 20. 0, 21. 5, 22. −3, 23. 7, 24. 15

Page 81 1. −12, 2. 4, 3. 25, 4. −4, 5. −16, 6. 8, 7. −5, 8. −21, 9. −24, 10. −2, 11. 7, 12. 27, 13. −6, 14. −18, 15. 15, 16. 5, 17. 40, 18. 4, 19. −32, 20. −7, 21. −30, 22. −3, 23. −5, 24. 36

Page 82 1. 173 ft, 2. 26°, 3. 10 °, 4. 20038 ft, 5. positive, 6. negative, 7. a. when b is even; b. when b is odd

Page 83 1. 10, 2. 7, 3. 56, 4. 35, 5. 25, 6. 4, 7. 24, 8. 0, 9. 12, 10. 27, 11. 36, 12. 21, 13. 19, 14. 17, 15. 21, 16. 16, 17. 16, 18. 9, 19. 9, 20. 24, 21. 3, 22. 5, 23. 12, 24. 13

Page 84 1. n = 46, 2. n = 16, 3. x = 58, 4. x = 23, 5. c = 68, 6. x = 21, 7. c = 10.6, 8. c = 21, 9. x = 120, 10. y = 103, 11. c = 63, 12. n = 87, 13. x = 121, 14. n = 115, 15. c = 6.5, 16. x = 144, 17. x = 27, 18. y = 7.9, 19. a = 1.6, 20. n = 42, 21. x = 19, 22. y = 43, 23. n = 96, 24. c = 3.6

Page 85 1. x = 17, 2. y = 11, 3. c = 44, 4. x = 8, 5. n = 12, 6. x = 26, 7. n = 8, 8. y = 23, 9. y = 4, 10. x = 3, 11. y = 6, 12. a = 6, 13. b = 205, 14. c = 130, 15. y = 288, 16. x = 192, 17. y = 512, 18. x = 660, 19. b = 253, 20. x = 192, 21. c = 470, 22. n = 2546, 23. x = 2100, 24. n = 3306, 25. c = 12, 26. x = 16

Page 86 1. $188, 2. 4.4, 3. 9, 4. 5, 5. 14 ft, 6. 90, 7. $150

Page 87 1. 1/2, 2. 1/2, 3. 1/3, 4. 2/3, 5. 1/6, 6. 1, 7. 1/52, 8. 1/52, 9. 1/26, 10. 1/13, 11. 1/2, 12. 2/13, 13. 1/4, 14. 1/26, 15. There might be 60 green and 40 brown leaves in there.

Page 88

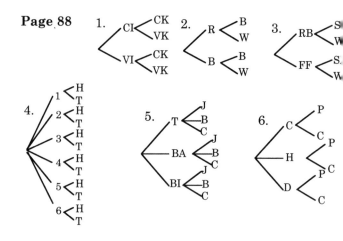

Page 89 1. Cars Sold at Baker Dealership, 2. months, 3. number of cars sold, 4. June, 5. January, 6. June & July, 7. 170, 8. Winter; fewer cars were sold then.

Page 90 1. 4.1; 4; 2, 4 2. 11.4, 12, 14 3. 23.1, 23, 23 4. 31.7, 29.5, none 5. 49.6, 45, 42 6. 48, 56, none 7. 10.9, 9.5, 8 8. 132.5, 137.5, none 9. 182.1, 175, none 10. 307.1, 350, 350

Page 91 1. 4%, 2. yes, 3. 3%, 4. George: 33 1/3%; Sister: 20%, 5. CD's: 36; clothes: 18, 6. 16, 7. 130